UNDER THE SEA

SENIOR AUTHOR

JACK BOOTH

DAVID BOOTH

WILLA PAULI & JO PHENIX

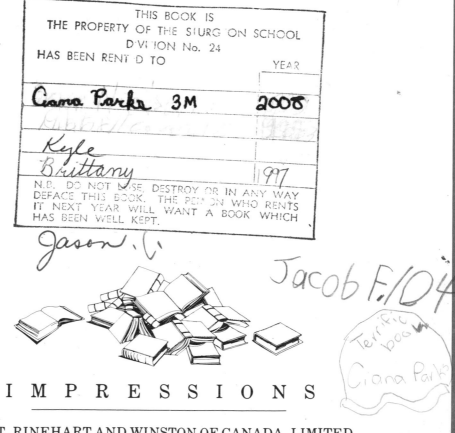

IMPRESSIONS

HOLT, RINEHART AND WINSTON OF CANADA, LIMITED

Project Editor: Wendy Cochran
Developmental Editor: Diane Taylor
Production Editor: Jocelyn Van Huyse
Art Director: Wycliffe Smith
Cover Illustrator: Heather Cooper

ISBN: 0–03–921504–0

Canadian Cataloguing in Publication Data

Main entry under title:
Under the Sea

(Impressions)
For use in schools.
ISBN 0-03-921504-0

1. Readers (Primary).   2. Readers—1950—
I. Booth, Jack, 1946—   II. Series

PE1119. U52 1985   428.6   C83-098253-1

Illustrations
Christine Bunn: pp. 6-7, 29; *Tina Holdcroft*: pp. 8-10; *Marc Brown*: pp. 11-21, 126-135; *Frank Modell*: pp. 22-28; *Arnold Lobel*: pp. 30-31, 32-33, 34-35; *Sami Suomalainen*: pp. 36-41; *Risto Turunen*: pp. 42-51; *Miro Malish*: pp. 52-53, 75-81; *Jerzy Kolacz*: pp. 54-55; *Beatriz Vidal*: pp. 56-69; *Ron Berg*: pp. 70-74; *Magda Markowski*: pp. 82-87, 215; *Stephen Harris*: pp. 88-89; *Peter Kovalik*: pp. 90-91; *Bernadette Lau*: pp. 92-101; *Wendy Kindred*: pp. 102-107; *Vesna Krystanovich*: pp. 108-115; *Barbara Griffin*: pp. 116-123; *Jeff Jackson*: pp. 124, 125; *Sylvie Daigneault*: pp. 136-137, 144-151; *Philip Mallette*: pp. 138-142; *Jock MacRae*: p. 143; *Michael Reinhart*: pp. 152-163; *Chris Workman*: pp. 164, 175; *James Walker*: pp. 165-174; *David Cousins*: pp. 176-182; *E. H. Shepard*: pp. 183-195; *Joanne Fitzgerald*: pp. 196-197; *Louise Cussack*: pp. 198-201, 202, 203; *Laura Fernandez*: pp. 204-214; *Julian Mulock*: pp. 216-219; *Barbara Klunder*: p. 220; *Barry Rubin*: pp. 221, 230; *Shelley Browning*: pp. 222-229; *Frank Hammond*: pp. 231-241; *John Lim*: pp. 242-256.

The authors and publishers gratefully acknowledge the consultants listed below for their contribution to the development of this program:

Isobel Bryan   *Primary Consultant   Ottawa Board of Education*
Ethel Buchanan   *Language Arts Consultant   Winnipeg, Manitoba*
Heather Hayes   *Elementary Curriculum Consultant   City of Halifax Board of Education*
Gary Heck   *Curriculum Co-ordinator, Humanities   Lethbridge School District No. 51*
Ina Mary Rutherford   *Supervisor of Reading and Primary Instruction   Bruce County Board of Education*
Janice M. Sarkissian   *Supervisor of Instruction (Primary and Pre-School)   Greater Victoria School District*
Lynn Taylor   *Language Arts Consultant   Saskatoon Catholic School Board*

Printed in Canada   7 8 9 10 11 12   92 91 90 89 88

Acknowledgements

Talk to the Animals: Words & Music by Leslie Bricusse. © 1967 TWENTIETH CENTURY MUSIC CORPORATION. All rights controlled and administered by UNART MUSIC CORPORATION. All Rights of UNART MUSIC CORPORATION Assigned to CBS CATALOGUE PARTNERSHIP. All Rights Controlled by CBS UNART CATALOG. International Copyright Secured. All Rights Reserved. *What's So Funny, Ketu?*: Text copyright © by Verna Aardema, pictures copyright © 1982 By Marc Brown. Reproduced by permission of the publisher, E. P. Dutton, Inc. *One Zillion Valentines*: By Frank Modell. Copyright © 1981 by Frank Modell. By permission of Greenwillow Books (A Division of William Morrow & Company). *Lavender's Blue*: Yaroslava Surmach Mills, "Lavender's Blue" from I LIKE YOU AND OTHER POEMS FOR VALENTINE'S DAY. Copyright © 1976 Yaroslava Surmach Mills. Reprinted with the permission of Charles Scribner's Sons. *The Hen and the Apple Tree* By Arnold Lobel (text and art) from FABLES, Written and Illustrated by Arnold Lobel, A Caldecott Medal Winner. Copyright © 1980 by Arnold Lobel. By permission of Harper & Row, Publishers, Inc. *The Elephant and His Son*: By Arnold Lobel (text and art) from FABLES, Written and Illustrated by Arnold Lobel, A Caldecott Medal Winner. Copyright © 1980 by Arnold Lobel. By permission of Harper & Row, Publishers Inc. *The Young Rooster*: By Arnold Lobel (text and art) from FABLES, Written and Illustrated by Arnold Lobel, A Caldecott Medal Winner. Copyright © 1980 by Arnold Lobel. By permission of Harper & Row, Publishers, Inc. *Mightiest of Them All*: By Meguido Zola © Meguido Zola. *Bringing the Rain to Kapiti Plain*: Text copyright © 1980 by Verna Aardema; pictures copyright © by Beatriz Vidal. Reproduced by permission of the publisher, E.P. Dutton, Inc. *Kenji Moto the Hermit*: By Alan Romanoff from Cricket Magazine. © 1979 Alan Romanoff; reprinted by permission of the author. *This Land is Your Land*: Words and Music by Woody Guthrie. TRO—© Copyright 1956 (renewed 1984), 1958 and 1970 Ludlow Music, Inc., New York., N.Y. Used by permission. *The Piney Woods Peddler*: Told by George Shannon. Copyright © 1981 by George W.B. Shannon. By permission of Greenwillow Books (A Division of William Morrow & Company). *Ida's Idea* By Wendy Kindred. Copyright © 1972 by Wendy Kindred. Reprinted by permission of the publisher, McGraw-Hill Book Company. *The April Rabbits*: By David J. Cleveland, text © 1978 by David J. Cleveland, reprinted by permission of Coward, McCann & Geoghegan. *Rain*: By Dionne Brand. Copyright © 1979 by Dionne Brand, published by Kids Can Press, Toronto, Canada. *Hurricane*: By Dionne Brand. Copyright © 1979 by Dionne Brand, published by Kids Can Press, Toronto, Canada. *Why the Tides Ebb and Flow*: From WHY THE TIDES EBB AND FLOW by Joan Bowden, illustrated by Marc Brown. Copyright © 1979 by Joan Bowden. Copyright © 1979 by Marc Brown. Reprinted by permission of Houghton Mifflin Company. *The Singing Bird*: By Barbara Resch. Adam & Charles Black (Publishers) Limited for Peggy Blakeley's text for THE SINGING BIRD by Barbara Resch. *If*: By Bernice Orawski. Reprinted by permission of the author. *Miracle for Maggie*: By Jean Little. Reprinted from SURPRISE By Jean Little. Used by permission of the author. *Samuel*: By Bobbie Katz. Copyright © 1972 by Bobbi Katz. Used by permission of the author. *Doctor Mary's Animals*: Developed by Beverley Allinson and Judith Lawrence, © Beverley Allinson and Judith Lawrence. Reprinted by permission of D.C. Heath. *My Dog*: By Bernice Aylen. Reprinted with permission of the poet. *A Bumpy Ride for a Bear*: By Shirley Benton Kerr. Copyright © 1974. All rights reserved. Published by permission of the author. *Pooh's Alphabet*: From THE WORLD OF POOH by A.A. Milne, illustrated by E.H. Shepard, copyright 1926, 1928 © 1957 by E.P. Dutton; renewed, 1954, 1956 by A.A. Milne; and POOH'S ALPHABET BOOK © 1975 by the Trustees of Pooh Properties. Reprinted by permission of the publisher, E.P. Dutton, Inc, *Stamp Collecting*: By Vincent Wong. Permission granted to print by Benjamin Wong. *Stamps of Canada*: STAMPS REPRODUCED COURTESY OF CANADA POST CORPORATION. *The Collection*: By Meguido Zola © Meguido Zola. *Sally Can't See*: By Palle Petersen. Reprinted by permission of the publisher, Adam and Charles Black (Publishers) Limited. *Wishers*: By Dolores Hind. Reprinted by permission of Dolores Hind. *Meet the Beetles*: Reprinted from OWL Magazine with the permission of the Publisher, The Young Naturalist Foundation. *Hey, Bug!*: By Lilian Moore from I FEEL THE SAME WAY. Copyright © 1967 Lilian Moore. Reprinted with the permission of Atheneum Publishers. *No Matter*: By Lee Bennett Hopkins. Reprinted by permission of Curtis Brown Ltd. Copyright © 1974 by Lee Bennett Hopkins. *One Red Tomato*: By Roger Aske. Reprinted by permission of Roger Aske. *Cat*: By Mary Britton Miller. Originally from MENAGERIE by Mary Britton Miller. *What For You So Crazy?*: By Roger Aske. Reprinted by permission of Roger Aske. *Sally Can't See*: Adaptation entire text SALLY CAN'T SEE by Palle Petersen (John Day Co.) Copyright © 1974 by Palle Petersen. English translation copyright © 1976 by A & C Black Ltd. By permission of Harper & Row, Publishers, Inc.

Every reasonable effort has been made to trace the owners of copyrighted material and to make due acknowledgement. Any errors or omissions drawn to our attention will be gladly rectified in future editions.

Table of Contents

Talk to the Animals
by
Leslie Bricusse

If we could talk to the animals,
just imagine it,
chatting to a chimp in chimpanzee,
imagine talking to a tiger,
chatting to a cheetah,
what a neat achievement
it would be.

If we could talk to the animals,
learn their languages,
maybe take an animal degree,
we'd study elephant and eagle,
buffalo and beagle,
alligator, guinea pig and flea.

We would converse
in polar bear and python,
and we would curse
in fluent kangaroo.
If people asked us,
"Can you speak rhinoceros?"
We'd say, "Of courseros!
Can't you?"

If we conferred
with our furry friends,
man to animal,
think of all the things
we could discuss.

If we could walk with the animals,
talk with the animals,
grunt and squeak and squawk
with the animals,
and they could squeak
and squawk and speak
and talk to us.

What's So Funny, Ketu?
by
Verna Aardema

In Africa, near the Mountains
of the Moon, there once lived a man
named Ketu. He was a happy man.
A big laugh lived inside him.

But it was *that* that got him into trouble.
It happened like this.

One day Ketu heard his dog yelping,
kao, kao, kao, behind the hut.
He investigated and found the dog
worrying a harmless little snake.
Ketu scolded the dog and sent him
slinking off,   *prada, prada, prada,*
with his tail between his legs.

The little snake raised its head and said, "Thank you, Man. You are kind. I'm going to give you a gift."

Ketu laughed, *tu-e, tu-e, tu-e!*
"What can a small creature
like yourself give to me?" he asked.

"A magic gift," said the snake. "From now on, you will hear animals think. But you must not tell anyone, or you will die!"

Ketu was not sure he wanted
such a gift. He tried to protest.
But the little snake had vanished!

That night Ketu's wife, Nyaloti, put their baby
into her basket bed. She tucked a pacifier,
made from the neck of a tiny gourd,
into the baby's mouth. And she patted her to sleep,
pah, pah, pah. Then Ketu fastened
the door. And he and Nyaloti lay down
on their low beds along the walls of the hut.

Soon they heard a mosquito going *zeee*
around the door. And Ketu heard it
say to itself, "I know they're in there!
Fat, juicy people! But I can't find a big-enough crack!"

Ketu laughed, *ge-e, ge-e, ge-e.* He laughed so hard,
he rolled off his bed—GU-MAPP!

Nyaloti cried, "What's so funny, Ketu!"

"Nothing!" said Ketu as he climbed back into bed.
He could not tell her.

Soon a rat tried the door. It could not get in either.
But it found a hole under the roof and came in there.
Ta, ta, ta, went the little feet of the rat, back and forth
across the floor. Then Ketu heard it say to itself,
"I wonder where that so-so woman keeps her butter!"

Ketu exploded with laughter, *kye, kye, kye!* He laughed
so hard, he scared the rat. And it leaped up
onto Nyaloti's bed—TWUM—in the middle of Nyaloti!

"*A-a-a-a!*" she screamed. "Get that rat off me!"
The rat leaped to the wall and scurried out
through the hole.

Nyaloti sat up in bed. She said, "Ketu, I think
your big laugh made that rat jump on me!
What were you laughing about?"

"Nothing!" said Ketu. "It was nothing."

"Nothing! *Tuh!*" sniffed Nyaloti. For by then
the baby was crying, *ke-yaa, ke-yaa, ke-yaa.*
And Nyaloti had to get her back to sleep.

The next morning Ketu fetched the cow from the shed
and tied her to a tree so that Nyaloti could milk her.
Soon he saw his wife coming with her big calabash bowl.
The cow saw her too. And Ketu heard her say to herself,
"Here she comes to steal my milk!
This time I just won't give any milk.
And my calf will drink it afterward!"

Ketu laughed, *ge-e, ge-e, ge-e!* He laughed so hard,
he scared the cow. And she galloped, *nun-tun, nun-tun,*
around the tree.

Nyaloti set the bowl down so she could scold
her husband with both hands.
She said, "What's so funny, Ketu?
Now you've frightened the cow with that silly laugh!
Were you laughing at me?"

"No," said Ketu as he walked away. "It was nothing."
The cow did not give any milk. Nyaloti didn't get a drop
in her bowl.

But the calf drank from her mother until her belly
was round and fat. It was as if she knew the saying,
Lest good food wastes, let the belly bust.

That evening at milking time the cow still would not give milk.
Nyaloti called Ketu. "Look," she said, "no milk again.
Our baby is ill for want of it.
That calf is killing our daughter!"

The cow swung her big head around and looked at Nyaloti.
And Ketu heard her say to herself.
"What! *My* daughter is killing *her* daughter!"

Ketu tried to hold back the laughter. But it burst out
between his fingers, *gug, gug, gug!*

The cow was so startled, she kicked and sent the bowl
rolling, *denki, denki, denki,* in the dirt.

"Now see what you did!" cried Nyaloti.
"You and that stupid laugh.
I'm going to tell the chief."

Nyaloti told the chief. The chief called Ketu
and all his wise men to the Tree of Justice
in the middle of the village. Nyaloti came too,
with the baby in a basket on her head.
And many other people came, just to hear the palaver.

"Ketu," said the chief, "your wife tells me you laugh
when there is nothing to laugh about. Is that true?"

"Oh, Chief," said Ketu, "I never laugh without a reason.
But I can't tell the reason. If I tell, I will die!"

"Nonsense!" exclaimed the chief.
"Talking never killed anyone!"

Nyaloti said, "He laughs at me, Chief.
I'm the only one around."

"No," said Ketu. "It isn't that!"

"If you don't laugh at your wife, what do you laugh about?"
demanded the chief.

Someone shouted, "Tell us, Ketu. We want to laugh too!"

The chief said, "Ketu, if you will not tell,
your wife will have to take the baby and go back
to live with her father."

Ketu's head drooped. He dug his toe into the sand
at his feet, *sa, sa, sa.* He didn't know what to do.
Just then his baby began to cry, *ke-yaa, ke-yaa, ke-yaa!*
Ketu watched as Nyaloti lowered the basket and lifted out
their beautiful baby. The pacifier he had made dangled
from the baby's fat little wrist.

Suddenly Ketu knew that no matter what happened
he could not let his wife and baby go. So he told
about the little snake, the magic gift,
and the funny thoughts of the animals.
Then KWAM! He fell over dead!

"Look!" cried the oldest wise man. "We made him do
what he should not have done. And he has had to pay
with his life!"

Nyaloti and many of the women began to wail,
wolu, wolu, wolu! The chief shook his head sadly.

Presently the little snake appeared.
It put its shiny head on Ketu's head. Ketu opened
his eyes. He turned his head in time to see
the little snake wriggle off into the weeds.
And he heard it say to itself, "Snoopy! That's what they are!
They can't let a man keep a secret!"

Ketu laughed, *kye, kye, kye!* He rolled on the ground
with laughter. The oldest wise man bent over him
and asked, "What's so funny, Ketu?"

The chief cried, "Don't ask him *that!*"

And Nyaloti said, "Laugh all you want, Ketu.
I'll never make palaver about it again!"

Then all the people began to laugh.
They laughed so hard, they scared the baby.
And above the sound of laughter
was heard the crying of the baby,
KE-YAA, KE-YAA, KE-YAA!

One Zillion Valentines
by
Frank Modell

One of Marvin's favourite days
was Valentine's Day.
"If I had a lot of money,
I'd buy all those valentines,"
said Marvin.

"That's silly," said Milton.
"You don't even have a girl."

"Valentines aren't just for girls.
Valentines are for everybody,"
said Marvin. "If I were a pilot,
I'd draw a great big one
in the sky."

"No one ever sent me a valentine," said Milton.

"That's because you never send any," said Marvin.
"If you don't send any, you don't get any."

"I never have any money," said Milton.
"Valentines cost money."

"You don't have to buy valentines,
you can make them.
All you do is get a lot of paper
and draw a big heart
like this," said Marvin.

"I can do that," said Milton.

"Anyone can do it," said Marvin.
"I bet we could make a zillion
valentines. One for everybody
in the neighbourhood."

"A zillion is a lot of valentines," said Milton.
"We better start right away."

Milton went to his house and got out his paint set,
his scissors, and coloured paper. Marvin went to his house
and got out his crayons, coloured pencils,
and a lot of paper.

They made valentines with big hearts, little hearts,
skinny hearts, fat hearts, polka dot hearts, striped hearts,
red hearts on white paper, and white hearts on red paper.

"Now what do we do?" said Milton.

"We send them to everybody," said Marvin.

"That's silly," said Milton. "We'll need a zillion stamps."

"No we won't," said Marvin. "We'll put them under people's doors. I'll take this side of the street and you take the other."

The next morning everybody in the neighbourhood was surprised to find a valentine under the door.

"We have lots left over," said Milton. "I guess
we made too many."

"No we didn't," said Marvin.
"People like to send valentines too.
They don't just like to get them."

"They are all gone," said Milton.

"Great," said Marvin.

"Maybe," said Milton. "But I bet we don't get
a valentine from anyone."

"Sure we do," said Marvin. "Follow me."

"A happy Valentine's Day to you, Milton."

"A happy Valentine's Day to you, Marvin."

Lavender's Blue
Anonymous

Lavender's blue, dilly, dilly, lavender's green,
   When I'm a King, dilly, dilly, you shall be Queen;
Who told you so, dilly, dilly, who told you so?
   'Twas mine own heart, dilly, dilly, that told me so.

Call up your men, dilly, dilly, set them to work,
   Some with a rake, dilly, dilly, some with a fork;
Some to make hay, dilly, dilly, some to thresh corn,
   While you and I, dilly, dilly, keep ourselves warm.

If it should hap, dilly, dilly, if it should chance,
   We shall be gay, dilly, dilly, we shall both dance;
Lavender's blue, dilly, dilly, lavender's green,
   When I'm a King, dilly, dilly, you shall be Queen.

The Hen and the Apple Tree

by
Arnold Lobel

One October day, a Hen looked out her window.
She saw an apple tree growing in her backyard.

"Now that is odd," said the Hen. "I am certain
that there was no tree standing in that spot yesterday."
"There are some of us that grow fast," said the tree.

The Hen looked at the bottom of the tree.
"I have never seen a tree," she said, "that has ten furry toes."
"There are some of us that do," said the tree. "Hen, come
outside and enjoy the cool shade of my leafy branches."

The Hen looked at the top of the tree. "I have never seen
a tree," she said, "that has two long, pointed ears."
"There are some of us that have," said the tree.
"Hen, come outside and eat one of my delicious apples."
"Come to think of it," said the Hen, "I have never heard
a tree speak from a mouth that is full of sharp teeth."
"There are some of us that can," said the tree. "Hen, come
outside and rest your back against the bark of my trunk."

"I have heard," said the Hen, "that some of you trees
lose all of your leaves at this time of the year."
"Oh, yes," said the tree, "there are some of us that will."
The tree began to quiver and shake. All of its leaves
quickly dropped off.

The Hen was not surprised to see a large Wolf in the place
where an apple tree had been standing just a moment before.
She locked her shutters and slammed her window closed.

The Wolf knew that he had been outsmarted.
He stormed away in a hungry rage.

It is always difficult to pose as something that one is not.

The Elephant and His Son
by
Arnold Lobel

The Elephant and his son
were spending an evening at home.
Elephant Son was singing a song.

"You must be silent," said Father Elephant.
"Your papa is trying to read his newspaper.
Papa cannot listen to a song while he is reading
his newspaper."
"Why not?" asked Elephant Son.
"Because Papa can think about only one thing at a time,
that is why," said Father Elephant.

After a while, Elephant Son asked,
"Papa, can you still think
about only one thing at a time?"
"Yes, my boy," said Father Elephant, "that is correct."
"Well then," said Elephant Son,
"you might stop thinking about your newspaper
and begin to think about the slipper
that is on your left foot."

"But my boy," said Father Elephant,
"Papa's newspaper is far more important
and interesting and informative
than the slipper that is on his left foot."
"That may be true," said Elephant Son,
"but while your newspaper is not on fire from the ashes
of your cigar, the slipper that is on your left foot
certainly is!"

Father Elephant ran to put his foot in a bucket of water.
Softly, Elephant Son began to sing again.

Knowledge will not always take the place of simple observation.

The Young Rooster
by
Arnold Lobel

A young Rooster was summoned to his Father's bedside.
"Son, my time has come to an end," said the aged bird. "Now
it is your turn to crow up the morning sun each day." The young
Rooster watched sadly as his Father's life slipped away.

Early the next morning, the young Rooster flew up to the roof
of the barn. He stood there, facing the east. "I have never done
this before," said the Rooster. "I must try my best."
He lifted his head and crowed. A weak and scratchy croak
was the only sound he was able to make.

The sun did not come up. Clouds covered the sky,
and a damp drizzle fell all day. All of the animals
of the farm came to the Rooster.

"This is a disaster!" cried a Pig.
"We need our sunshine!" shouted a Sheep.
"Rooster, you must crow much louder," said a Bull.
"The sun is 150 million kilometres away.
How do you expect it to hear you?"

Very early the next morning, the young Rooster flew
up to the roof of the barn again. He took a deep breath,
he threw back his head, and crowed. It was the loudest crow
that was ever crowed since the beginning of roosters.

The animals on the farm were awakened from their sleep
with a start. "What a noise!" cried the Pig.
"My ears hurt!" shouted the Sheep.
"My head is splitting!" said the Bull.

"I am sorry," said the Rooster, "but I was only doing my job."
He said this with a great deal of pride, for he saw, far to the east,
the tip of the morning sun coming up over the trees.

A first failure may prepare the way for later success.

Mightiest of Them All

by
Meguido Zola

Once there was, and twice there wasn't, a hare,
a little hare, a little snowshoe hare. In a thicket
she was born; under the drooping, snow-laden branches
of some saplings overlooking the edge of the prairie.

On a moonlit night, when the last of the big snow
had emptied the sky, she first looked out
onto the strange new world that sparkled white
and cold and still. High on her hind legs
she stood, bright eyes peering curiously about,
nose trembling, whiskers aquiver, ears raised high
and twitching back and forth.

Then, in one hop, leap, and bound, she was off and away;
in another, she was in the open meadow; in another,
she was sunk in the soft, powdery snow,
high over her haunches, deep up to her ears.

The hare, the little hare, the snowshoe hare, cried out,
"Snow, Snow, you fall so gently, you fall so silently,
and you cover everything about. Tell me, Snow,
are you mightiest of us all?"

But the Snow only sighed, "Hare, little hare,
snowshoe hare, if I were mightiest of us all,
tell me, how could the chinook wind breathe on me
and warm me and melt me to nothingness?"

So the hare crossed the prairie to where the sun's fiery ball
sinks to rest at the close of day.

And there, where the plains begin to roll and pitch
their long climb into the hills, she called to the Chinook,
"Wind, Wind, who has seen you, and who can tell
from where you have come and where you will go?
And yet you blow where you will, and you warm
everything you touch. Tell me, Wind, are you mightiest
of us all?"

But the Chinook only whistled mournfully,
"Hare, little hare, snowshoe hare, if I were mightiest
of us all, tell me, how could the mountains catch me
and hold me and chase me out through the narrow eye
of the pass?"

So the hare climbed the mountain top that towers high
and sheer above the prairie.

And there, where the narrow pass twists and winds its way
among the soaring peaks, she asked, "Mountain, Mountain,
you tip the sky, you pierce the clouds, and you dwarf
everything so far about. Tell me, are you mightiest
of us all?"

But the Mountain only rumbled, "Hare, little hare,
snowshoe hare, if I were mightiest of us all, tell me,
how could the earth make me tremble, make me quake,
raise me up and bring me low?"

So the hare dug into the earth, deep into the bowels
of the earth below.

And there, where the earth melts
into the ever-burning furnace of fire, she cried out,
"Earth, Earth, you are ever restless in your depths,
and you move and you shake and you fold the mountains
up above. Tell me, are you mightiest of us all?"

But the Earth only whispered, "Hare, little hare,
snowshoe hare, if I were mightiest of us all, tell me,
how could the herbs and the grasses send down their roots
through me, and how draw up their roots through me?"

So the hare went back to the place where she had been born,
in the thicket, under the drooping snow-laden branches
of saplings overlooking the edge of the prairie.

And now, among the fields and banks and drifts of snow,
there peeped out a crocus, first flower of the Spring.
And the hare asked, "Crocus, Crocus, you spring
from the soil and you flower the earth. Tell me,
are you mightiest of us all?"

But the Crocus only shook its blossom, "Hare, little hare,
snowshoe hare, if I were mightiest of us all, tell me,
how could you pluck me, and nibble me, and eat me?"

So the hare jumped for joy and leaped and gambolled
as she cried out, "The snow may fall and cover everything
about; and the wind may melt the snow; and the mountains
may stop the wind; and the earth may move the mountains;
and the herbs and grasses may overrun the earth.
But I, the hare, the little hare, the snowshoe hare,
I pluck the first flower of the Spring, I nibble on it
and I eat it, and I am mightiest of them all."

A War Between the Dog and the Wolf

translated by
Victoria Symchych and Olga Vesey

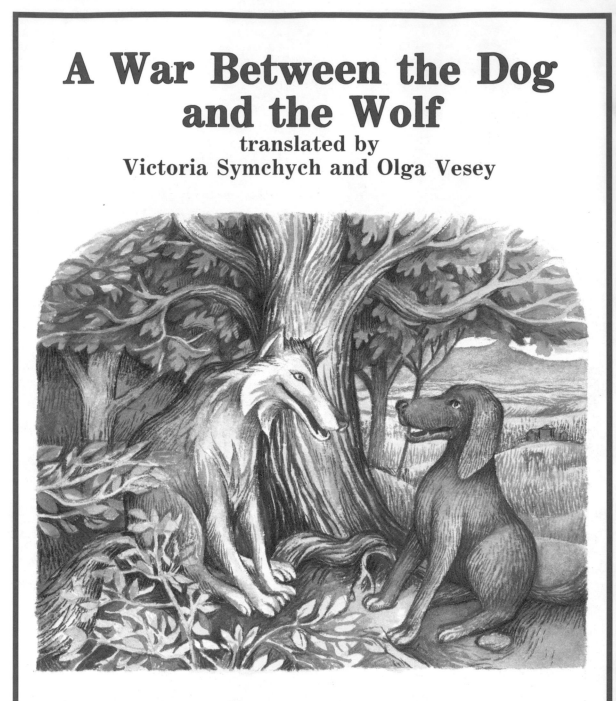

Once there lived a dog and a wolf who were best friends.
Every day they met under an old oak tree
at the edge of the forest. They would spend hours
exchanging news. The dog would tell the wolf
what was happening on his master's farm
and the wolf told the dog all the news of the forest.

One day the wolf said to the dog, "Listen, my friend,
I hear that your master's pig just had a litter of piglets."

"That's true. Just think!
Twenty little piglets in one litter.
And all of them are so fat and pink and healthy!"

"You are making me hungry just talking about it,"
said the wolf. "I must go see them tonight."

"No, my friend, don't do that," said the dog. "We agreed
that we would meet here, and that I would tell you
all the news, but you would never come to my master's farm.
If you break your promise, we couldn't be friends any longer."

"Why should we fight over such a small thing?
Twenty little piglets! If I made off with one
or two who would ever know the difference?"

"Please, my friend. Don't come to my master's yard.
I am afraid you will make trouble."

"What kind of trouble?" asked the wolf. "Don't worry.
I will slip into the barn so quietly that no one
will hear me."

"But I will hear you."

"You? But you are my friend. You will be loyal to me."

"That's easy enough for you to say. But don't forget
that my master is my friend also. He looks after me
and feeds me. How can I be disloyal to him?
What will he think of me then?"

"That's your problem," said the wolf.
"I must have the piglets for my supper tonight,
so take my advice and be very quiet about it."

Night came and the wolf kept his word. He crept up
to the barnyard and slipped into the barn. The dog saw him
and thought to himself, ''What am I to do? I'll wait awhile.
If the wolf does it quietly, I shall be quiet also.
But if he makes the slightest noise, I shall let
my master know about it.''

No sooner was the wolf in the barn than the mother pig
began to squeal. Soon all twenty piglets were squealing too.
The dog added a long howl to the chorus which awakened
his master. The farmer ran into the barn and gave
the wolf such a beating that the wolf could hardly move.

Several days later the wolf limped to the barn gate
and snarled at the dog, "A fine friend you are!
Just you wait. I'll fix you!"

"I told you not to come to my master's yard," said the dog.

"And I told you to be quiet," argued the wolf.

"Yes, but you said no one would hear you, remember?
As long as I didn't hear anything I was quiet.
Then you started a fight with the mother pig."

"Who started a fight with the mother pig?
No sooner did I get into the barn than she started to squeal.
Listen, my friend, I just have to have one of those piglets
for supper tonight. Promise me you will not give me away?"

"I promise," answered the dog. "But remember,
you must be quiet in the barn. If I hear
the slightest noise I will howl so loud,
you will be able to hear it all the way to the forest."

At midnight the wolf set out for the farm. But before
he could reach it, the dog warned the mother pig
that he was coming. As soon as the wolf slipped
into the barn the pigs made such a noise, and the dog
howled so loudly that the wolf barely had time
to escape another beating.

Several days passed. Then the dog saw his friend again
outside the barnyard gate.

"Pssst. Come here," whispered the wolf.
"Why don't you come out into the forest anymore?
Have you forgotten your friend?"

"No, I haven't," answered the dog simply.

"Oh, you traitor!" sneered the wolf. "Do you think
I will forget what you've done to me? I know you warned
the mother pig. Just wait—one day you will be sorry."

"We'll see. I knew our friendship could not last forever.
But I'll get even with you one day," answered the dog.

"You will get even with me? You miserable creature!
How dare you make fun of me," screamed the wolf.
"I hereby declare war. Three days from now we shall
gather our armies and meet by the old oak tree.
But if you are a coward and do not come,
my army will come here and drag you out
by the ears and tear you to pieces!"

With that the wolf turned and loped off into the forest.
He went straight to the bear's den and, bowing very low,
said, "My friend, I have come to ask a favour of you.
The dog has betrayed our friendship and I have declared
war on him. Will you help me?"

"Very well," said the bear. "I shall be there when you need me."

Then the wolf found the wild boar and said, "In three days I must go to war against the dog. Will you help me?"

"Of course, of course," grunted the boar.

The wolf asked the fox to be in his army also. They all agreed to meet on the third day by the old oak tree.

Meanwhile the dog was very worried.
"What shall I do? Where can I get an army?" he sighed.
Two days passed. The dog could not eat or sleep.

The old barn cat saw the dog becoming worse and worse.
Finally he said, "What's the matter with you?
Why are you looking so miserable?"

"I am in very bad trouble and you won't be able
to help me," answered the dog.

"Tell me about it and then we'll see if I can help
you or not."

So the dog told the old cat all about his war
with the wolf.

"Now, now, my friend. It's not so bad.
I will help you," said the cat.
"Go call the gander and the drake.
Don't look so doubtful. I'm sure we'll win."

The dog was not convinced, but he did
as he was told, and the drake
and the gander promised to help.

Finally the day set for the war came.
Early in the morning before the sun was up,
the dog and his friends set out from the farm.
First came the gander marching proudly,
holding his head high. He kept time by calling,
Tra ta-ta! Tra ta-ta! just like an army drum.
Behind him marched the dog and the cat
with their tails straight up. Last came the drake
keeping time with his constant,
Tok tok-tok! Tok tok-tok!

In the forest, the wolf and his army met by the old oak tree. The wolf told the bear to climb the tree. He told the boar to bury himself in a pile of dry leaves. The fox was to stand on guard nearby while the wolf hid behind the tree.

Soon they saw something coming towards them through the darkness.

"Here they come!" called the bear. "Listen to their drums!"

"And look," said the fox. "Behind the drums are two soldiers. See how their long guns stick up high in the air! This will be the end of us."

"We must fight," said the wolf. "Besides, we can't leave our hiding places now. It's too late."

As the farm animals marched towards the tree, the cat saw something move under the pile of leaves.
"A mouse!" he thought. The cat's paws shot forward and his claws sank into the boar's tail.
A huge bellow of pain came from under the pile of leaves. The cat was so terrified he raced up the tree.

The bear, hearing something coming after him, climbed further up to the top of the tree. But the branches were too thin to hold him. *Crash!* Down came the bear and landed on the ground with a great thud.

In the middle of all the excitement, the dog spotted
the fox's tail and grabbed it. "Ouch!" cried the fox
and ran away so fast he left his tail behind.
The rest of the wolf's army was now so frightened
that they all ran away in different directions.
The farm animals watched them go and then marched
happily back to the farm.

The wolf's army met again deep in the forest. The wolf said
to his friends, "How could we fight them
when they had guns with them?"

"Look at me," the boar cried. "I lost part of my tail."

"The bomb they threw blew my tail right off," said the fox.

The bear cried sadly, "I don't know what happened to me.
But I do know I landed on my seat and it is still sore.
I shall never try to fly again."

Marco Polo, Everyone

by
David Booth

Rumpelstiltskin, children!
Let's all Mowgli.
Kublai Khan, my people!
Marco Polo me.

I will take you places,
Come and hold my hand.
Step inside the story,
Know a magic land.

Underneath the mountain,
Far above the sea,
Journey with the story,
Wander there with me.

Seek the great adventure,
That the story gives.
Sail my ship of wonder,
Marco Polo lives!

Rumpelstiltskin, children!
Let's all Mowgli.
Kublai Khan, my people!
Marco Polo me.

Bringing the Rain to Kapiti Plain

by
Verna Aardema

This is the great
Kapiti Plain,
All fresh and green
from the African rains—
A sea of grass for the
ground birds to nest in,
And patches of shade for
wild creatures to rest in;
With acacia trees for
giraffes to browse on,
And grass for the herdsmen
to pasture their cows on.

But one year the rains
were so very belated,
That all of the big wild
creatures migrated.
Then Ki-pat helped to end
that terrible drought—
And this story tells
how it all came about!

This is the cloud,
all heavy with rain,
That shadowed the ground
on Kapiti Plain.

This is the grass,
all brown and dead,
That needed the rain
from the cloud overhead—
The big, black cloud,
all heavy with rain,
That shadowed the ground
on Kapiti Plain.

These are the cows,
all hungry and dry,
Who mooed for the rain
to fall from the sky;
To green-up the grass,
all brown and dead,
That needed the rain
from the cloud overhead—
The big, black cloud,
all heavy with rain,
That shadowed the ground
on Kapiti Plain.

This is Ki-pat,
who watched his herd
As he stood on one leg,
like the big stork bird;
Ki-pat, whose cows
were so hungry and dry,
They mooed for the rain
to fall from the sky;
To green-up the grass,
all brown and dead,
That needed the rain
from the cloud overhead—
The big, black cloud,
all heavy with rain,
That shadowed the ground
on Kapiti Plain.

This is the eagle
who dropped a feather,
A feather that helped
to change the weather.
It fell near Ki-pat,
who watched his herd
As he stood on one leg,
like the big stork bird;
Ki-pat, whose cows
were so hungry and dry,
They mooed for the rain
to fall from the sky;
To green-up the grass,
all brown and dead,
That needed the rain
from the cloud overhead—
The big, black cloud,
all heavy with rain,
That shadowed the ground
on Kapiti Plain.

This is the arrow
Ki-pat put together,
With a slender stick
and an eagle feather;
From the eagle who happened
to drop a feather,
A feather that helped
to change the weather.

It fell near Ki-pat,
who watched his herd
As he stood on one leg,
like the big stork bird;
Ki-pat, whose cows
were so hungry and dry,
They mooed for the rain
to fall from the sky;
To green-up the grass,
all brown and dead,
That needed the rain
from the cloud overhead—
The big, black cloud,
all heavy with rain,
That shadowed the ground
on Kapiti Plain.

This is the bow,
so long and strong,
And strung with a string,
a leather thong;
A bow for the arrow
Ki-pat put together,
With a slender stick
and an eagle feather;
From the eagle who happened
to drop a feather,
A feather that helped
to change the weather.

It fell near Ki-pat,
who watched his herd
As he stood on one leg,
like the big stork bird;
Ki-pat, whose cows
were so hungry and dry,
They mooed for the rain
to fall from the sky;
To green-up the grass,
all brown and dead,
That needed the rain
from the cloud overhead—
The big, black cloud,
all heavy with rain,
That shadowed the ground
on Kapiti Plain.

This was the shot
that pierced the cloud
And loosed the rain
with thunder LOUD!
A shot from the bow,
so long and strong,
And strung with a string,
a leather thong;
A bow for the arrow
Ki-pat put together,
With a slender stick
and an eagle feather;
From the eagle who happened
to drop a feather,
A feather that helped
to change the weather.

It fell near Ki-pat,
who watched his herd
As he stood on one leg,
like the big stork bird;
Ki-pat, whose cows
were so hungry and dry,
They mooed for the rain
to fall from the sky;
To green-up the grass,
all brown and dead,
That needed the rain
from the cloud overhead—
The big, black cloud,
all heavy with rain,
That shadowed the ground
on Kapiti Plain.

So the grass grew green,
and the cattle fat!
And Ki-pat got a wife
and a little Ki-pat—

Who tends the cows now,
and shoots down the rain,
When black clouds shadow
Kapiti Plain.

Kenji Moto the Hermit
by
Alan Romanoff

There once was a man in Japan named Kenji Moto.
Kenji was a hermit by choice, for he had been crippled
as a boy and had decided to live alone on the side
of a hill, rather than stay among people who might pity
or scorn him. So, slowly and painfully, he tilled
a small rice field for food and to trade for fish
in the nearby village.

From his humble house on the hill, Kenji could see
the village of his birth, nearly an hour's walk away.
And just beyond the village was the ocean, stretching out
as far as the eye could see.

The villagers were mostly fishermen who hauled their living
from the ocean. A few of the men and most of the women
and children worked in the rice fields which reached
from the edge of the village to the slope
just below Kenji's hut.

One afternoon as Kenji was toiling in his field, he paused
for a moment's rest and gazed out toward the ocean.
His casual glance became an intense stare as he saw
something strange and frightening on the horizon.

The sky above the ocean was threateningly dark, and the ocean
itself seemed to be rising up to engulf the sky. Kenji looked
in wonderment, trying to understand what was happening.

Suddenly, he knew what the darkened sky and towering waters
meant. Many years ago, long before anyone now living
in the village had been born, a tidal wave had come rushing
in from the sea, and Kenji had heard his grandfather tell how,
within an hour, the entire village had been swept away
and the land covered with ocean water.

"I must warn the villagers," thought Kenji. "But how?
By the time I could get down there with my crippled leg,
the tidal wave would be upon them." Desperately, he looked
around for some method to signal a warning, but nothing
was large enough to be seen that far away.
Then, an idea came to him.

"A fire!" he thought. "A fire would be seen from far away."
Kenji knew of only one thing large enough to make a fire
that bright. So he lit a torch and, with quiet resignation,
set fire to the rice crop he had cultivated so painfully
and that meant life itself to him.

Within seconds the field was ablaze, and Kenji retreated
some distance away. When he turned his attention
toward the steadily darkening sky, he saw tnat the wall
of water was much closer and guessed that the full impact
of the tidal wave would strike within the hour. Anxiously,
Kenji stared down at the village. "They have to see
the fire," he muttered. "They have to!"

Meanwhile, in the village below, many eyes had spotted
the fire on the hill, and an excited crowd had gathered.

"It's Kenji's rice field," said one man.

"Yes," agreed another, "and if the fire spreads,
it will take all our fields."

"We must hurry and put out the fire, or there will be
no rice for any of us this year."

And so within minutes, all the villagers were hastening
toward the top of the hill. Even those who were too young
or too old to help fight the fire went along to watch.

From his position on the hillside, Kenji saw the parade
making its way up the slope and compared it to the progress
of the oncoming wave. "Why don't they hurry?" he worried
aloud. "The big wave is almost here."

As the villagers climbed higher and higher, they were able
to see the wall of water for the first time. Swift runners
were sent back to the village to gather important records
and to make certain that everyone had left, and the rest
of the group hurried even faster up the hill.

When the villagers arrived at Kenji's house,
they gathered around him.

"It's fortunate that your rice field caught fire," said one, "for it brought us here, safe from the giant wave."

"How did the fire get started?" asked another.

"With this," said Kenji quietly, holding up the charred and smoking torch.

Only then did the villagers realize that Kenji had deliberately set fire to his field in order to warn them. And not even the most eloquent among them could find words to express their gratitude.

Silently everyone turned to watch the huge wave draw nearer and nearer. When it struck, it would destroy everything they owned. But thanks to Kenji, they were saved and they would rebuild.

And each of them silently vowed that there would always be a place in his new home for Kenji Moto, the hermit.

The Proud King and the Stubborn Duke

retold by
Larry Swartz

There once was a king who was proud and powerful.
Unfortunately he was used to having his own way.
Among the lords of his realm was a duke.
This duke was just as proud as the king and just as stubborn.

Everytime the king would say "You must,"
the duke would answer "I won't." This so angered the king
that at last he decided to call together his horsemen,
his archers, and his swordsmen. He ordered them all
to bring out his machines of war. And so, the proud king,
riding at the head of his army, set out to teach
the stubborn duke a lesson.

Meanwhile, the duke, who had been warned of the king's plans,
was busy in his castle making preparations for battle.
He received much help from the country folk who lived
on his lands. Long ago these people promised to defend
his castle whenever danger threatened. As a reward,
the duke offered these people protection
behind the high castle walls. When the duke called
for help, the country folk hurried to him
with all they could carry of the things they owned.

They stored away food and water, enough to last
for many days. They sharpened their spears,
tested their bows, and took their places.
And so, the duke, like the king, had an army.
When all was ready, with a man behind each loophole
the others high atop the walls, the duke was satisfied.
"BAR THE GATES!" the duke shouted, and his orders echoed
around the castle walls.

At the very moment that the gates slammed shut,
the king's horsemen galloped toward the castle with spears
upraised. His archers were lined up—eager to let loose
their arrows. A battering ram and a sling for hurling rocks
were being rolled forth, creaking and groaning
on the heavy wheels.

Then, for days, the battle continued, but each day
the duke's loyal men fought off the enemy.
The walls stood firm; the gates held fast.
The army, made up of country folk,
remained strong.

But days turned into weeks and the food supply in the castle
grew less and less. The duke's people, though brave,
were very hungry because they could only have
one small meal each day. They began to complain.
"Our stomachs growl with hunger, while in our fields
the hare is having a picnic with our cabbages
and the deer feasts on our corn. We must go
and chase the animals away before all our food
is stolen."

But no one could leave the castle.
The duke was not one to surrender.

Among the people were shepherds
who could be seen gazing out the castle windows
with hopes of seeing their flocks.
"No one is there to watch our wandering sheep.
Who's to save the lambs from the prowling wolves?"
they cried.

Still, no one could leave the castle.
The duke was not one to surrender.

The women, too, began to mourn.
"The looms in our empty cottages stand unused.
Only spiders are left to spin and weave,
and cobwebs won't warm us when winter comes."
The women, like their fathers, husbands, and grown sons,
begged the duke to surrender. But the stubborn duke ordered
his men to fight on. And on.

The king himself was beginning to grow impatient, and one day,
wearing his royal crown and carrying his royal sword,
he rode up to the castle gate. "I command you to surrender,"
he called to the duke.

"I refuse!" was, of course, the reply.

"You leave me with no choice," the king answered.
"I shall burn down your castle, and put all your men
to battle with their swords." However, he added these words:
"Send the women and children through the gates
and they will not be harmed."

The women began to shake. They turned to the duke's wife
to tell them what to do. The duchess begged her husband
to surrender and save them all.
But the duke was too proud and too stubborn to surrender.

The women begged and begged their own husbands
to surrender. The men loved their wives, and indeed
their own lives, but they would not go against the duke.
The cries of the women rose up, "All is lost! All is lost!"
Seeing all the tears and stubbornness about her,
the duchess remarked, "What we need is a plan."

Moments later, a message was sent to the king.
In this message, the duke's wife thanked the king
for saving the lives of the women and children.
Included in this message was one small favour
the duchess asked of the king.
"Let each woman carry out the thing she most treasures."

The king agreed. "Yes, whatever they can take."

The duchess was pleased. The women were joyous!
They quickly began sorting through their many belongings,
each woman wondering what she should take.

"My best boots."

"My fine woven shawl."

"This gown with golden threads."

"This copper pot used by my grandmother."

One by one the women named their treasures,
only to toss them away.

"What good are these? These things do not matter
when all else is lost!" the women cried.

The duchess ordered the women to be calm.
She said, "These things you own are nothing
but trinkets. You must decide what is dearest to you
in all the world. Then you will know what to carry
out of the castle."

Later, the gates swung open. The women came out,
each one carrying her dearest treasure.
As the crowd of women came forth, the king
and his army could not believe what they saw.
As the king watched the women struggling
with their heavy loads, tears came to his eyes.
"Well done!" he cheered. "Well done!"

"Well done," repeated his soldiers.

The castle was restored to the duke and the duchess.
Forever after, the king treated them with honour,
affection, and respect.

The Indian Cinderella
retold by
Jo Phenix

Once, in olden times, there dwelt a great Indian chief.
People used to say that he was one of Glooscap's helpers,
but no one really knew.

He had a strange and wonderful power; he could make himself
invisible. While he was invisible, he would mingle
with his enemies, and overhear their plots.
People called him Strong Wind the Invisible.

Strong Wind lived with his sister in a tent near the ocean.
His sister helped him in his work. Many maidens wanted
to marry him because of his great deeds. They knew
that Strong Wind would marry the first maiden
who could see him as he came home at night. Many had tried,
but for a long time none of them had succeeded.

Strong Wind used a trick to find out if a maiden was telling
the truth. His sister was the only one who could see him.
Every evening his sister would walk along the beach
to meet him. Any maiden who wished to take the test
would walk with her.

When his sister saw him coming, she would ask the maiden,
"Do you see him?"

The maiden would falsely answer, "Yes."

Then the sister would ask, "What is pulling his sled?"

The maiden would say, "The hide of a moose," or "A pole,"
or "A great cord."

Then the sister would know that the maiden was lying because these were only guesses. Strong Wind would not marry a maiden who lied.

In a nearby village lived a great chief
who had three daughters. The youngest of the daughters
was very beautiful and sweet-tempered and was loved
by everyone. Her sisters were jealous of her, and treated
her cruelly. They tried to make her look ugly. They made
her dress in rags and cut off her long black hair.
They took coals from the fire and burned her face
so she would have scars. The young girl did not complain,
but went about her work as usual.

One evening the two older daughters decided to try
Strong Wind's test. When Strong Wind's sister asked
if they could see him coming, each one answered
"Yes."

Then the sister asked, "What is his shoulder strap made of?"

The sisters guessed and said, "Rawhide."

Later they looked in the tent where Strong Wind was eating
supper. They could see the coat and moccasins
he had been wearing, but they could not see him.
They went home alone and disappointed.

One day, the younger daughter decided that she would try
to win Strong Wind. She tried to make herself look pretty.
She patched her dress with birchbark,
put on the few ornaments she owned,
and set off. All the people laughed at her,
and her sisters called her a fool. She took
no notice of them, and continued on her way.

Strong Wind's sister welcomed her kindly, and took her
to the beach. When Strong Wind came, his sister said,
"Do you see him?"

The girl spoke the truth. "No!" she said.

Strong Wind's sister asked again, "Do you see him now?"

"Yes," replied the girl, in a frightened voice,
"and he is very wonderful."

"With what is he pulling his sled?" asked the sister.

The girl answered, "With a rainbow."

"What is his bowstring made of?" asked the sister.

The girl answered, "His bowstring is the Milky Way."

Then Strong Wind's sister knew that the girl was telling
the truth and that Strong Wind had allowed her to see him.
She took her home and bathed her. All the scars disappeared
from her face, and her hair grew long and beautiful.
She gave her fine clothes to wear.

When Strong Wind entered the tent he sat beside her
and called her his bride. She became his wife
the next day, and from that time onward
helped him in his work.

The girl's sisters were angry. Strong Wind decided
to punish them. He changed them both into aspen trees,
and rooted them to the spot. Since that day,
whenever Strong Wind approaches, aspen trees tremble
and shiver in fear, for they remember his great power,
and their cruelty to their sister long ago.

This Land Is Your Land

by
Woody Guthrie

This land is your land
This land is my land.
From Bonavista
To Vancouver Island
From the Arctic Circle
To the Great Lake waters,
This land was made for you and me.

As I was walking
That ribbon of highway,
I saw above me
That endless skyway,
I saw below me
That golden valley,
This land was made for you and me.

I've roamed and rambled,
And I followed my footsteps,
To the fir-clad forests
Of our mighty mountains,
And all around me
A voice was sounding,
This land was made for you and me.

This land is your land
This land is my land.
From Bonavista
To Vancouver Island
From the Arctic Circle
To the Great Lake waters,
This land was made for you and me.

The Piney Woods Peddler
by
George Shannon

Once, back a ways, lived the Piney Woods peddler.
He travelled through the woods and up and down the rivers.
Wherever he went, he was swapping and trading. He'd trade
anything he had except his dear darling daughter.
He loved her more than words can tell.

One day his dear darling daughter said, "Daddy,
get me a shiny silver dollar so I can buy some pretty things."

"Yes, indeed," said the peddler, "and soon to boot!"
He hopped on his horse and rode off to find a dollar.

The frogs were a-croaking. The birds were a-flying
and the peddler was soon a-singing:
   "With a wing wang waddle
   And a great big straddle
   And a Jack-fair-faddle
   It's a long way from home."

Before long he met a barefoot woman with a big brown cow.
Said the Piney Woods peddler to the barefoot woman:
   "Trade you my horse
   Trade you my ring
   For a shiny silver dollar
   I'll trade anything."

Woman said, "Got no shiny silver dollar, but we can trade
just the same—my big brown cow for your big black horse."
So the Piney Woods peddler swapped his horse for the cow
and off he went.

The woodpeckers were a-pecking and the peddler walked
a-singing:
  "With a wing wang waddle
  And a great big straddle
  And a Jack-fair-faddle
  It's a long way from home."

Now along came a man with a strong black mule.
Said the Piney Woods peddler to the strong mule-man:
  "Trade you my cow
  Trade you my ring
  For a shiny silver dollar
  I'll trade anything."

Mule-man said, "Got no shiny silver dollar, but we can trade
just the same—my strong black mule for your big brown cow."
So the Piney Woods peddler swapped his cow for the mule.

The bees were a-buzzing and the peddler walked a-singing:
    "With a wing wang waddle
    And a great big straddle
    And a Jack-fair-faddle
    It's a long way from home."

Soon came a boy with a fine hunting dog.
Said the Piney Woods peddler to the hunting-dog boy:
    "Trade you my mule
    Trade you my ring
    For a shiny silver dollar
    I'll trade anything."

Boy said, "Got no shiny silver dollar, but we can trade
just the same—my fine hunting dog for your strong mule."
So the Piney Woods peddler swapped his mule for the dog.

The flies were a-flitting and the peddler walked a-singing:
    "With a wing wang waddle
    And a great big straddle
    And a Jack-fair-faddle
    It's a long way from home."

By and by came a man with a big wood stick.
Said the Piney Woods peddler to the wood-stick man:
    "Trade you my dog
    Trade you my ring
    For a shiny silver dollar
    I'll trade anything."

The man said, "Got no shiny silver dollar, but we can trade
just the same—my big wooden stick for your fine hunting dog."
So the Piney Woods peddler swapped his dog for the stick.

The wind was a-whistling and the peddler walked a-singing:
    "With a wing wang waddle
    And a great big straddle
    And a Jack-fair-faddle
    It's a long way from home."

Then along came a rattlesnake rattling all his rattlers.
Said the Piney Woods peddler to the long rattlesnake:
"Trade you my stick
Trade you my ring
For a shiny silver dollar
I'll trade anything."

Snake said, "Got no shiny silver dollar, but I've got teeth
of poison. I'll take your stick instead!"

That snake jumped at the stick and bit down hard.
His teeth went so deep he couldn't get them out.
The peddler didn't worry.

He just picked up that stick and swung it around and around
and up and down till that snake went flying by the trees.

Then the Piney Woods peddler smiled and walked off
a-singing:
  "With a wing wang waddle
  And a great big straddle
  And a Jack-fair-faddle
  It's a long way from home."

Now as he sang, his stick began to swell.
The snake's poison was spreading through the wood.

The more the poison worked, the more the stick swelled.
It was soon as big as two trees—three trees—four.

About this time came a railroad man.
Said the Piney Woods peddler to the railroad man:
    "Trade you my stick
    Trade you my ring
    For a shiny silver dollar
    I'll trade anything."

The man said, "I've got a shiny silver dollar
and I'd be glad to make the trade."

"Good," said the peddler, "I knew I'd get a dollar
for my dear darling daughter. Here's the stick.
Where's the dollar?"

"Don't have it with me," said the man.
"Tell you what I'll do. I'll bring it
to your house tomorrow before noon."

The peddler walked home a-singing as happy as could be:
    "With a wing wang waddle
    And a great big straddle
    And a Jack-fair-faddle
    It's a long way from home."

The railroad man cut and chopped the stick
into three hundred and three strong railroad ties.
He was pleased with the trade.

That night there came a storm—
a great big storm.
It rained so hard it washed the poison
out of the wood. As the poison washed out,
the swelling went down.
Those ties got smaller and smaller and smaller still.
When the sun came up, they were
no bigger than toothpicks.

The railroad man ran to the peddler's house
way before noon. "Your stick shrunk down.
It's not worth a dollar. It's barely worth a dime!"

"Let me see that dime!" cried the dear darling daughter.
She held it to the light and it shone like a star.
"I like it," said the daughter.
"It's like a shiny silver dollar,
but dear and darling like me!"

"You can keep it," said the peddler, "and I'll start
trading again for your shiny silver dollar."

He kissed her goodbye and set off down the road.
And all the while he walked, he kept on a-singing:
    "With a wing wang waddle
    And a great big straddle
    And a Jack-fair-faddle
    It's a long way from home...."

Ida's Idea
by
Wendy Kindred

Ida Strummer lives in the city with her mother.
One day Ida came home from school and found
a maple sugar candy doll on her bed.
Beside it was a note which said:

For Ida
My name is
Mabel.
Eat me slowly

Ida said to her mother, "Hey, Mom, did you see anyone
putting anything in my room today?"

Her mother said, "No, I didn't see anyone coming or going."

Then Ida bit off one of Mabel's legs, held it in her mouth,
closed her eyes, leaned her head back and dreamed
of maple sugar snow falling softly all around her
in the kitchen. When she opened her eyes,
there was nothing left in her mouth but maple sugar juice,
so she swallowed it. Then she laid Mabel gently
in her wrapper and looked around for a safe place
to put her.

She said, "Hey, Mom, where's a good place to put
my maple sugar doll so she will be safe from flies
and cockroaches and mice and robbers?"

Her mother said, "How about in the refrigerator
where she won't melt?"

So Ida put her there.

Every time anyone opened the refrigerator door,
the first thing they saw was maple sugar Mabel
with one leg missing. Before Ida went to bed,
she opened the refrigerator door to say Good Night
to Mabel, and when she got up, she opened
the refrigerator door to say Good Morning.

But in the morning, Mabel was missing two legs.
In fact, she had no legs left at all.

Ida said, "Hey, Mom, did you see anyone in the kitchen
last night?"

And her mother said, "No, I didn't see anyone
coming or going."

So Ida went to school.

When she came home, she opened the refrigerator door,
took Mabel out, and bit off one maple sugar arm.
She held it in her mouth, closed her eyes,
spread out her arms, and twirled in slow circles
in the maple sugar snow falling all around her
in the kitchen until she was dizzy and there was nothing
left in her mouth but maple sugar juice.
Then she swallowed it.

Before she went to bed that night, she opened
the refrigerator door to say Good Night to Mabel
with no legs and one arm. When she got up, she opened
the refrigerator door to say Good Morning.

But in the morning, Mabel was missing two legs
and two arms. In fact, she had no legs and no arms
left at all.

So Ida said to her mother, "Hey, Mom, are you sure
you didn't see someone in the kitchen last night?"

And her mother said, "No, I didn't see anyone
coming or going."

Ida went to school.

When she came home, she opened the refrigerator door
and bit off half the body of maple sugar Mabel.
Then she lay down on the floor and closed her eyes
and made angel wings with her arms
in the maple sugar snow on the kitchen floor
until there was nothing left in her mouth
but maple sugar juice, and she swallowed it.

Before she went to bed, she opened the refrigerator door
to say Good Night to the head and half the body
of maple sugar Mabel, and when she got up, she opened
the refrigerator door to say Good Morning. But in the morning,
all that was left was Mabel's head smiling up at her.

Ida said to her mother, "Mom, who was in the kitchen last night?"

And her mother said, "I didn't see anyone in the kitchen
last night."

So Ida went to school. All day long she thought
about how to save the head of Mabel. By the time she got home
she had thought of an idea. She went straight to her piggy bank
and shook it upside down until a penny fell out.

Then she took the penny to the gum machine on the corner
and bought a ball of bubble gum. When she got back,
she wrote a note saying:

FOR MOM — MY NAME
is B. GUM. CHEW ME SLOWLY.

She put the ball of bubble gum, unchewed, and the note
beside each other on her mother's bed.

Before Ida went to bed, she opened the refrigerator door
to say Good Night to Mabel's whole head. When she got up,
she opened the refrigerator door to say Good Morning.
In the morning the whole head was still there
smiling up at her. She popped it in her mouth,
squeezed her eyes closed, and wished with all her might
that she had another maple sugar doll. She wished
and wished until there was nothing left in her mouth
but maple sugar juice. So she swallowed it.

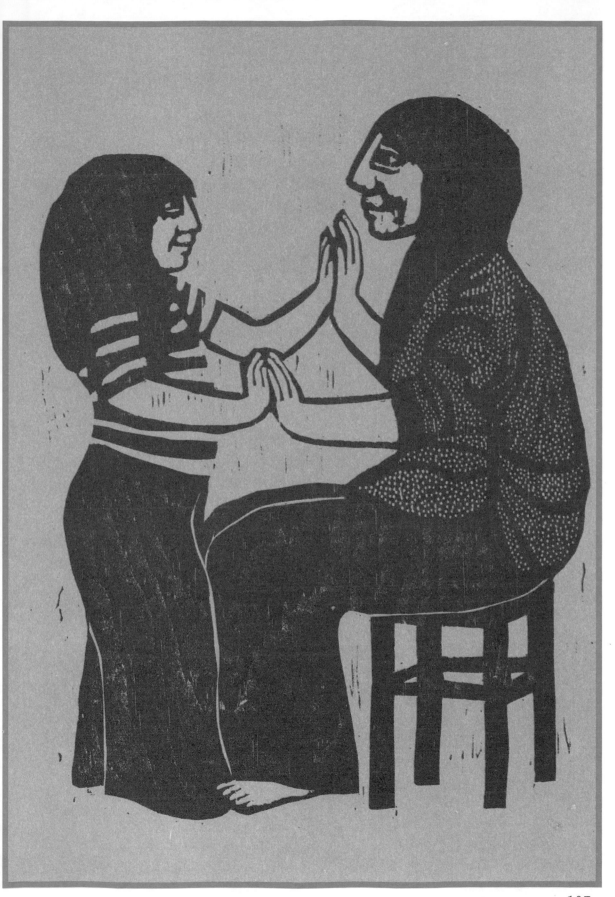

The April Rabbits

by
David Cleveland

On the first day of April the sun was shining, birds were chirping, and a rabbit was nibbling on a bush as Robert went off to school.

On the second day of April Robert scared two rabbits across the road as he walked to his tuba lesson.

On the third day of April he thought for a minute that he saw three rabbits in skirts tap-dancing on the windowsill.

On the fourth day of April
he felt there was something
rabbity about the living room
as he watched TV.

On the fifth of April Robert found
five half-eaten carrots
at the very bottom
of his toy box.

While fishing on the sixth, he saw
six rabbits paddle by in a canoe.

On the seventh day of April
there were seven rabbits
singing with a cat
on the garage roof.

Eight rabbits left their bikes
in the driveway on the eighth.

All nine seats at the soda fountain
were taken by rabbits on the ninth,
but they made room for Robert.

On the tenth Robert noticed
ten funny holes in the lawn
as he took out the garbage
for his mother.

On the eleventh of April
eleven rabbits on skateboards
whizzed down Elm Street.

There were twelve rabbits playing
basketball at the playground
on the twelfth.

On the thirteenth there were thirteen rabbits
in the supermarket.

There were fourteen rabbits
at the clothesline
on April fourteenth.

On the fifteenth Robert's mother
took him to the eye doctor
because she thought he was seeing things.
There were fifteen patients ahead of him.

On the sixteenth Robert found sixteen rabbits making double-decker peanut butter and radish sandwiches in the kitchen.

Seventeen rabbits in Scout uniforms marched by in a line on the seventeenth.

On the eighteenth Robert thought he spotted a flock of eighteen rabbits fly over his head and land in a nearby tree.

On the nineteenth of April nineteen tiny rabbits jumped
out of a bag of pretzels and ran in all directions.

On the twentieth of April twenty rabbits in funny hats
gave a birthday party in the dining room.

There were twenty-one rabbits with him
on the ferris wheel at the amusement park
on the twenty-first.

On the twenty-second, twenty-two crazy rabbits
tried on all his clothes, including
his favourite baseball cap.

Robert found twenty-three rabbits
taking a nap in his bedroom
on the twenty-third.

The next day a busload of twenty-four rabbits stopped
next to him at the corner and all the passengers
made faces at him through the   window.

Twenty-five rabbits all took out books
ahead of him at the library on the twenty-fifth,
but he still got the book he wanted.

On the twenty-sixth, twenty-six rabbits
took a bath in his tub and used up
all the bubble bath.

In the movies on the twenty-seventh,
Robert sat in the midst
of twenty-seven rabbits
crunching popcorn.

On the twenty-eighth of April
twenty-eight rabbits camped out
all night in the backyard,
telling stories and roasting
a giant head of lettuce on the campfire.

On the twenty-ninth day of April
twenty-nine rabbits with suitcases
tiptoed down the driveway and out of sight.

On the last day of April Robert watched very carefully
all day long, but he didn't see a single rabbit.
Anywhere.

That night, a hippopotamus followed him home.

The Price of Eggs
by
Mary Ann Nicholson

Characters:

WIDOW   NEIGHBOUR   STRANGER   JUDGE

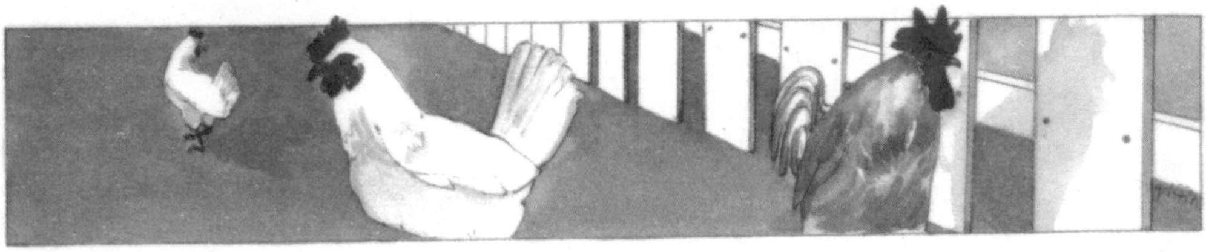

Scene One

Time: A spring morning.

Setting: A village street. The widow is sweeping
the door step in front of her house and stops to greet
her Neighbour, who is passing on her way to market.

WIDOW:
   Good day to you, Neighbour. I see you are off to market.
NEIGHBOUR:
   And good day to you, Widow. I have not seen you
   for a long while, not since your late husband's funeral.
WIDOW:
   May heaven keep him.
NEIGHBOUR:
   How do you get along these days, Widow?
WIDOW:
   I make do, though I do have to work hard. I have my goats
   and my chickens. With the money I get from selling
   the eggs, I buy more chickens. I'm not starving.

NEIGHBOUR:

> Indeed, you are a lucky woman to be able to say that.
> My husband has gone away to the iron mines. He sends
> home his week's pay for me to buy food and shoes
> for our children. But it is never as much as we need.

WIDOW:

> Times are hard for everyone. Every day I see a stream
> of men going past the door on their way to work
> in the iron mines. Look, here comes one now.

STRANGER:

> I beg your pardon, my good woman, but I must sit down.
> I am too weary to walk another step without rest.

NEIGHBOUR:

> You must have come a long way. I suppose
> you are on your way to find work
> in the iron mines like all the others.

STRANGER:

> Yes, I am on my way to the mines. I have walked
> from a village beyond this one
> and still have a long way to go.

WIDOW:

> You may rest awhile on my doorstep if you wish;
> it's clean and it's free.

STRANGER:
    Thank you, madam. If I had some food,
    I might have more strength to continue my journey.
    Could you spare a crust of bread, kind woman?
    I have had nothing to eat all day.

WIDOW:
    I have little enough to eat myself. I am a poor widow
    alone in the world. I cannot help every stranger who passes by.

NEIGHBOUR:
    You could sell him some of your eggs, Widow.
    Take pity on him, he is so tired and hungry.
    Surely, you can't refuse him a little kindness.
    Remember, we, too, know what it is to be hungry. Help him.

WIDOW:
    I could sell you a dozen eggs.
    They were fresh from under the hens
    this morning. You could eat them on your way.

STRANGER:
    How wonderful they would taste, but I have no money
    to pay you for them. I cannot give you anything.
    But I promise to pay at some later date.

WIDOW:

I would be a fool to do business that way.

NEIGHBOUR:

Good Widow, how can you be so greedy?

He is starving and you do nothing.

Give him some eggs.

WIDOW:

Give him eggs? Certainly not. How you talk!

No wonder you are always poor.

NEIGHBOUR:

Then accept his promise to pay.

He has an honest face.

I'm sure you can trust him.

WIDOW:

All right, but he will have to take yesterday's eggs,

which I cooked this morning. I shall get a good price

for my best fresh eggs in the market.

STRANGER:

Cooked eggs will be very welcome,

and I won't have to worry about breaking them.

Thank you, kind Widow. You have my word of honour

that I will pay for the eggs when I come back

this way again, no matter how long it takes me

to make my fortune at the iron mines.

NEIGHBOUR:

Heaven keep you, Stranger. *(Stranger leaves.)*

Don't you feel a little happier in your heart

for having helped a stranger, Widow?

WIDOW:

No, I only feel lighter in my purse. I will never see him

again, thanks to you. It's the last time

I'll listen to you.

NEIGHBOUR:

Heaven will bless you many times for your kindness

today, wait and see.

Scene Two

Time: Ten years later

Setting: Same as Scene One. The Stranger dressed
in fine clothes is walking with the Neighbour.

NEIGHBOUR:
   When I saw you in the marketplace,
   I didn't recognize you at first.
   Ten years can make a lot of difference in people.
   When you were here before, you were in rags.
STRANGER:
   I have been blessed with riches from my work
   in the iron mines. Now I am part owner of those mines.
   I can repay my debt to the widow who gave
   me a dozen eggs when I needed food.
   Does she still live here?
NEIGHBOUR:
   Yes, she does, but I rarely see her.
   She has become a miser and is so bitter
   with the world that she can't say
   a kind word about anybody. Paying your loan
   will please her very much.
STRANGER:
   (Knocks on Widow's door.)
   I hope it will be a happy surprise.
WIDOW:
   Who's there? Who's knocking?
STRANGER:
   It is I, good Widow. I have come to pay you
   for the dozen eggs you gave me ten years ago.
   You see, I have never forgotten your great kindness
   to me. I want to keep my promise to pay.
   Here are two bags of gold for you.

WIDOW:

Only two bags of gold? It will take all you have
to pay me after ten years.

STRANGER:

How can that be?

NEIGHBOUR:

I see trouble brewing for you, Stranger. I warned you
she had become greedy. I'll run and fetch the Judge.
He is wise in such matters.

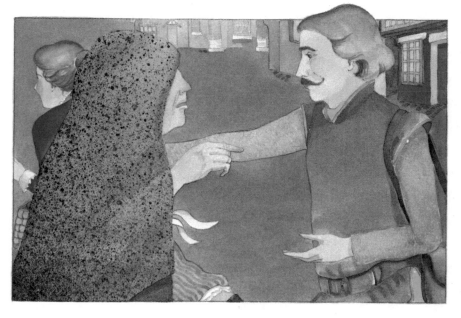

STRANGER:

Just a moment, old Widow. Your neighbour is fetching
a Judge. Perhaps he can solve this difficulty.
I don't understand why a dozen eggs should be worth
more than two bags of gold, even with interest
on the loan for ten years.

WIDOW:

The Judge will understand and protect
a poor widow's rights.

NEIGHBOUR:

Here is the Judge. Now you can tell him
your story, Widow.

WIDOW:

Well, Your Honour, if I had not given this man a dozen eggs,
I would have hatched a dozen chickens from them.
And from those dozen chickens, I would have had more eggs
and more chickens. In these ten years I would have had
thousands of chickens, and I, too, would be rich.

JUDGE:

What you say sounds logical enough.
Has she left any point out, Stranger?

STRANGER:

Not that I can see, Your Honour.

JUDGE:

Ahem, ahem, then I shall give my decision...

NEIGHBOUR:

Wait a minute, Your Honour. I have just remembered
something. *(She whispers excitedly to Judge. He looks
surprised and smiles.)*

JUDGE:

Before I make my decision, I want to ask the Widow
if she will do me one favour.

WIDOW:

What is that, Your Honour?

JUDGE:

Will you cook me some ears of corn? I'm thinking
of planting a garden.

WIDOW:

You must be joking, Your Honour. Everyone knows
you can't grow corn that has been cooked.

JUDGE:

Aha, there you see. Then you have forgotten that the eggs
you gave this stranger were hard-boiled. How did you think
you were going to hatch chickens from cooked eggs?

WIDOW:

You are right, Your Honour. I have been very foolish.
I will be happy with the two bags of gold the Stranger offered.

JUDGE:

Not so fast, old Widow. You should be taught a lesson
for your meanness. (*To Stranger*) Sir, pay her no more
than the price of a dozen hard-boiled eggs.

STRANGER:

If it's all right with you, Your Honour, I would rather give
her the two bags of gold to show my gratitude
to her for the kindness she showed me ten years ago.

JUDGE:

You are very generous and forgiving, Stranger.
I hope that after today, the Widow will know better
than to count her chickens before they are hatched.

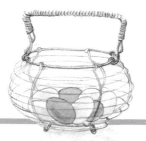

Rain

by
Dionne Brand

It finally came,
it beat on the house
it bounced on the flowers
it banged the tin roof
it rolled in the gutters
it made the street muddy
it spilled on the village
it licked all the windows
it jumped on the hill.
It stayed for two days
and then it left.

Hurricane

by
Dionne Brand

Shut the windows
Bolt the doors
Big rain coming
Climbing up the mountain.

Neighbours whisper
Dark clouds gather
Big rain coming
Climbing up the mountain.

Gather in the clotheslines
Pull down the blinds
Big wind rising
Coming up the mountain.

Branches falling
Raindrops flying
Tree tops swaying
People running
Big wind blowing
Hurricane! on the mountain.

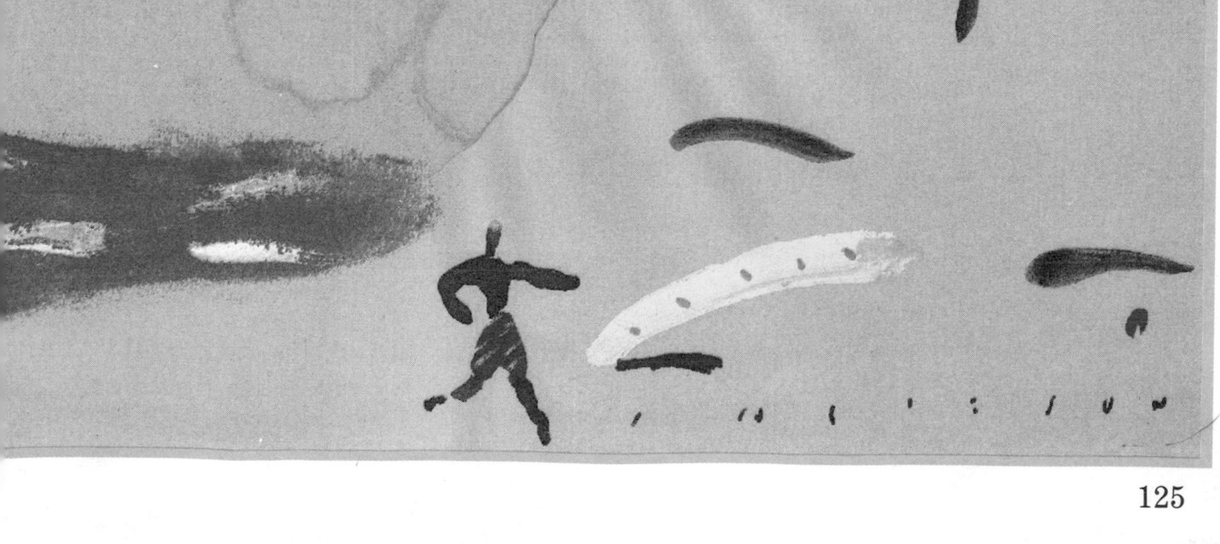

Why the Tides Ebb and Flow

by
Joan Chase Bowden

Not in my time, not in your time, but in the old time,
when the earth and sea were new, a stubborn old woman
had no hut. She lived all by herself
in the middle of a flower patch.

When the winds blew, she was cold. When the rains came,
she was wet. And when the sun shone down, she was neither
cold nor wet, but she was burned from top to toe.

So one day she called to the Sky Spirit
To-Whom-All-Things-Belonged, "O Great Spirit, I need a hut."

Sky Spirit was busy. He called down, "No hut today.
Maybe tomorrow."

But the next day, and for many days after that,
he was still too busy to send down a hut
for the stubborn old woman, but still she wanted one.

So another day, after thinking and thinking, Old Woman called,
"Then give me a rock to shelter me from the weather."

Sky Spirit was too busy to have been thinking and thinking.
Too quickly, he answered, "Take one."

Then how happy was the stubborn old woman. She knew
exactly which rock she wanted. So she climbed
into her stewpot and set sail on the great, green ocean.

She sailed along, and she sailed along, and soon she saw
Sea Bird.

He called:
　"Ai-ee, Old Woman,
　Listen to me.
　You are sailing too close
　To the hole in the sea."

"Oho!" answered Old Woman, "then I think I am sailing
in the right direction."

She sailed along, and she sailed along, and soon she saw
Little Silver Fish.

He called:
　"Ai-oo, Old Woman,
　Listen to me!
　You are much, much too close
　To the hole in the sea."

"Aha!" answered Old Woman, "then I know I am sailing
in the right direction."

She sailed along, and she sailed along, and soon
she reached the still, quiet place in the sea.
She looked down into the clear water,
and she saw a rock more beautiful than any
she had ever seen before.

"That is the rock I want," she said, and she reached down
to get it.

But at that very moment, busy Sky Spirit called to her
from his hut in the clouds:

"Old Woman, Old Woman,
Listen to me!
Don't take the rock
From the hole in the sea!"

Stubborn Old Woman answered, "But that's the rock I want!"
And she reached down and down.

Then Sky Spirit called again:
"Old Woman, Old Woman,
Are you listening to me?
I think you are taking
The rock from the sea."

Stubborn Old Woman answered, "But that's the rock I need!"
And she reached down and down.

Then Sky Spirit called for a third time:
"Old Woman, Old Woman,
You're *not* listening to me.
Be *sure* you don't take
The rock from the sea!"

Stubborn Old Woman answered, *"But you said I could have it!"*

And she pulled and pulled and pulled, until *fop!*
up came the rock from the ocean floor.

Then wasn't Sky Spirit sorry! With the rock gone,
the sea began to pour down and down into the bottomless pit
that was the hole in the sea.

Around and around in great circles went the water,
faster and faster. And around and around in her stewpot
went the little old woman, with the rock clutched
tight in her arms.

"Put it back!" cried all the creatures of the air, very frightened.

"Put it back!" cried all the creatures of the sea,
very much frightened, too.

"Put it back!" roared angry Sky Spirit from the clouds.

But the stubborn old woman would not put back the rock
into the hole in the sea. "It's mine now!" she said.

So Sky Spirit had to hurry and send Little Dog
down to earth.

"Go put your nose in the hole in the sea!"
commanded Sky Spirit. And Little Dog did.

But his nose was too small, and the water was too cold,
and down, down went the sea, *m'tia, m'toa, TLOP!*

The Old Woman took shivering Little Dog into her stewpot.
"From now on, you can be my little dog," she said,
"and I will love you always."

Then Sky Spirit had to hurry and send Young Maiden
down to earth.

"Go kneel in the hole in the sea!" he commanded.
And Young Maiden did.

But her knees were too small, and the water was too cold.
And down, down went the sea, *m'tia, m'toa, TLOP!*

Old Woman took shivering Young Maiden into her stewpot, too.
"From now on, you will be my daughter," she said,
"and I will love you forever."

For the last time, Sky Spirit had to hurry. He sent
strong Young Man down to earth.

"Go sit in the hole in the sea!" commanded Sky Spirit.
And strong Young Man did.

But still the hole was too big, and the water too cold.
And down, down went the sea as before, *m'tia, m'toa, TLOP!*

Then Old Woman also took shivering Young Man
into her stewpot. "From now on, you will be
my daughter's husband," she said, "and I will love you, too."

They all clung together in the stewpot as it spun
around and around in ever smaller circles,
closer and closer to the hole in the sea.

"Put back the rock!" cried all the creatures of the sea.

"Put back the rock!" cried all the creatures of the air.

"Put back the rock," cried Sky Spirit, "and I will let you borrow
it twice each day forevermore to pretty up your flower patch."

The stubborn old woman looked at Little Dog,
who would love and protect her. She looked at Young Maiden,
who would keep her company when the long day's work
was done.

She looked at strong Young Man, who would build her a hut!

And Old Woman smiled.

Then she leaned over and put back the rock into the hole
in the sea, *fom!*

The water stopped circling. The sea filled up and filled up.
And off home sailed the stubborn old woman,
with her loving family.

But twice each day, she still goes a-sailing in her stewpot.
Twice each day, she borrows the rock to pretty up
her flower patch.

As she takes the rock away, the water goes down and down
into the hole in the sea. That is low tide.

As she puts the rock back, the sea fills up and fills up.
That is high tide. To this day, that is why the tides
ebb and flow.

But some parts of Little Dog, Young Maiden, and Young Man
never did warm up.

To this day, that is why
all Little Dog's children have cold noses.
That is why all Young Maiden's daughters have cold knees.
And to this day, that is why all Young Man's sons stand
with their backs to the fire.

The Singing Bird
by
Barbara Resch

Under the palm tree sat the King whilst overhead the sun
burned down. "My, my," said the King, "it is very hot
today, and I am so thirsty." And he called his servant
to fetch him a pitcher of water from the river-bank.
"Servant," he said, "do go and fetch me a pitcher
of cool water." And off went the servant,
obedient to the King's command.

On the river-bank the servant was kneeling down to fill
the pitcher, when suddenly, overhead, he heard
some fluttering wings and some twittering and trilling.
And a beautiful bird hovered above him and began to sing.
The water quite forgotten, the servant listened
and then began to sway and dance to the beautiful music.

Meanwhile, back in the village the King was getting cross
and longing more and more for his drink of cool water.
So he called for his wife, the Queen. "Wife," he said,
"do go and find out what has happened to my servant."

And off she went, obedient to the King's command.
As she drew near the river-bank the Queen heard
the beautiful singing and was soon joining
in the swaying and dancing with the servant.

Meanwhile, back in the village the King was getting crosser
and longing more and more for his drink of cool water.
So he called for his son, the Prince. "Son," he said,
"do go and find out what has happened to the servant
and your mother, the Queen."

And off went the Prince, obedient to the King's command.
As he drew near the river-bank he heard the beautiful music
and was soon joining in the swaying and dancing
with the servant and his mother, the Queen.

Back in the village, the King grew more and more impatient.
"Bother," he said. "I shall go myself and find out
what has happened to my servant, my wife the Queen,
my son the Prince and my pitcher of water."
And off he went.

As he drew near the river-bank, the King too heard the singing of the beautiful bird and saw his servant, his wife the Queen, and his son the Prince, swaying and dancing to the music.

And soon he was moved to join in and as the bird sang his beautiful song, the King danced.

And as he danced, the King thought,
"I must have this bird for my own.
No other King has anything like it and people will come
from all around the countryside to hear this wonder."

And the King stopped dancing to whisper to his servant
to catch the bird. The servant reached out his hand
and the bird was caught.

And immediately the singing stopped and all was silent
on the river-bank. The dancing stopped too
and the King took the bird from the servant.
"Sing, bird, sing," pleaded the King.
But the bird was silent.

"Sing, bird, sing," begged the servant.
But the bird was silent.

"Why won't you sing?" asked the King's wife, the Queen.
But the bird was silent still.

"You must sing for my father," said the Prince, his son,
"for my father is a mighty King."
But the bird still kept silent.

At last the King, his wife the Queen and his son the Prince
started back to the village. The pitcher was full of water,
the day was still hot and the King was still cross.
But the servant stayed behind on the river-bank,
coaxing the bird to sing, but it would not.

Instead that beautiful bird gazed around
at all the wild creatures who were free,
the lion, the elephant, the fish in the river, the birds in the air.

And he kept his beautiful song for himself.

The servant thought, "The bird does not sing
because he's been captured.
I must set him free."

And he put the bird down gently on a green bush.
And the bird didn't pause, not even for a second.
He lifted his wings and soared into the air
and sang and sang and sang.

And he's singing still for all we know.

If
by
Bernice Orawski

If I wriggled my toes
into the ground,
If I held my breath
and made no sound,
If I stuck out my arms
like branches, so,
If I stood in the rain
so I would grow,
until my trunk
was as high as a tree,
Would a bird, do you think,
build a nest on me?

Miracle for Maggie
by
Jean Little

Some friends found the duck. He was lying on the beach
with his head on a log. He had been caught in the oil slick
from one of the big boats in Vancouver harbour,
and his feathers were drenched, choked with black oil.

Now he could swim no longer. He lay there helplessly,
waiting to die. The friends picked him up and carried him
to Maggie's mother.

Maggie and her brothers, Peter and Mark, all saw the duck
when he was brought into the house. He was so weak
he could not even lift his head. He lay as limply
as Maggie's Raggedy Ann doll.

"He must dive for his food," Maggie's mother said.
"He's half-starved, poor thing."

But first she had to clean off the suffocating oil.

Maggie and the boys watched, wide-eyed. Their mother put
the duck into the kitchen sink. Four times she washed him
with liquid detergent. Each time, she rinsed him off
afterward. He did not struggle.

"He knows we're trying to help him," Maggie thought,
but she wondered if he would ever be all right again.

"Now for some food," said Maggie's mother briskly.

She wrapped the duck up in a big bath towel and sat him on her lap. She took bits of fish—fish they had planned to have for supper!—and dipped them in milk.
Then she held up the duck's head and dropped them, one by one, into his open beak.

The children laughed with delight and relief as the fish went safely down his throat. He swallowed gratefully.

Was he a little stronger? Maggie could not tell.

"Let's see if he can swim," Peter suggested.

"Not yet," their mother said. "The detergent will have taken the natural oil out of his feathers too.
He needs that to swim."

The duck's head was hanging down again.

"He won't be able to swim tomorrow," Maggie thought sadly.

They shut him up safely for the night
where their cat could not get at him.

The next morning, Maggie's mother fed him again.
He held his own head up now and he moved his wings
under the towel.

"All right," Maggie's mother said at last, "I think
we can try him out in the bathtub."

Maggie held her breath.
Perhaps the poor duck would sink
like a stone.

Very slowly, weakly, crookedly, the duck paddled around
in the tub.

"He's swimming!" Peter cried joyfully.
"He's swimming."

Maggie smiled too but her eyes were worried.
The duck still seemed so tired. He did not look
at home in the tub.

They fed him twice more and then, tried him again.
This time, he had come alive, every feather of him.
He splashed wildly and shook himself.
The bathroom was wet from floor to ceiling.

Maggie sighed with relief.
Maggie's mother sighed too—
but Maggie knew she was really glad about it.

The next day, they fed the duck
as much fish as they could.
They let him have one last riotous swim.
Then the entire family took him down to the beach.

Maggie's mother held him so that he could see
the wide sweep of water. The duck made
excited noises and started moving his feet
and his wings in readiness.

"Away you go then," said Maggie's mother.

The duck took off into the waves
as though he were coming home after a long,
long time. He dove and dove.

His joy was so big, so wonderful, so free
that every part of Maggie sang with it.

She looked at her family.
Even Mark, the baby, was smiling widely.
Maggie turned back to scan the ocean.
He was gone.

"Let's go home. I'm cold," Peter said.

But Maggie was warm all the way home.

A Narrow Escape
by
David Booth

The little fox lay in the underbrush, alone and frightened.
Where was his mother? Where were his brothers and sister?
Where was his home?

It was daytime. During this time he usually slept,
curled up with his family. At night they all played together,
pushing and shoving each other and making up games.

But there was no one to play with now, no one to cuddle up to
and keep warm. No one to feed him, and he was hungry,
so hungry. He was only four weeks old, and his only food
was his mother's milk, and there was no mother and no milk.

The little fox began to whimper, because he was cold
and hungry and afraid. He had been born blind,
like all foxes, but now he could see.
However, this did not help, because he was lost.
Every bush looked the same, every tree was
the same tree, every sound was a strange sound.
He huddled under the leaves and cried softly.

It was dangerous to make any noise at all,
but the fox was too young to know that.
There were enemies all around,
and the little fox could not defend himself as yet.
But he was afraid, and so he could not stop whimpering.
Suddenly, he was quiet. He had heard something behind him.

His heart began to beat faster and faster.
Then the bushes parted and a snout was pushed at him.
He yelped and turned to see his mother, the vixen,
staring into his eyes.

She nuzzled the little fox and sniffed him all over.
He smelled the way that she had remembered,
the way that her other little kits smelled.
He was brown and woolly, and he snuggled up
to her. Because he was hungry, he searched
for her milk, and the mother began to feed
her little one. They were both happy now.

The little fox began to sleep, safely beside his mother
once more. But the vixen stayed awake, wide awake.
She knew the dangers nearby. She knew that they were not
in their own safe den. They were in the farmer's field,
and it was noon. Enemies could see her and her kit.

Why had he not run away at night?
Her eyes could almost see in the dark.
That is when she hunted; the darkness was her friend.
Now, she was out in the daylight, far from her den.
She would have to carry the little fox in her teeth.
He could not run as fast as she could,
and she could not leave him here.

She knew that if she had to, she would die for the little fox.
She looked at him sleeping, and then carefully picked
him up. They would have to make the journey now.
There were three other kits waiting for her
in the den. They were not safe without her.

She knew the farm well. She had made her den in the woods
nearby. A badger had left his hole, and the vixen had made
it larger, to fit her family. She had lived there
for three years. It seemed very far away
at this moment.

Then she heard it. It wasn't a new sound to her; she had
heard it many times before. The dog. The farmer's dog.
The barking was far off, but it was getting nearer all the time.
She had to leave at once. She had to run for her life.
And for the life of the little fox. And for the lives
of the three small ones alone in the den.
She did just that. She ran and ran.

It was the most frightening sound the vixen had ever heard.
As the dog ran, it kept baying, "I am coming, Fox, I am coming!"
It was on her trail, sniffing out her scent, following her.

It was hard for the vixen to run carrying the little one,
but she would never leave him. And the dog was getting
closer. And closer. The fox did not come to the farm
very often. Last year, she had come one chilly night
with her mate and killed a chicken. This year,
she had decided to stay away from the farm.
Until the little one had run away.
Until now.

She was into the woods, heading for the stream, for safety.
Then she saw it. The dog was in the woods, too, on her trail.
She held on tightly to the little one, and she ran and ran.

Suddenly, she doubled back to trick the dog. But it found
the scent and took off after her. The fox had learned
to live by her wits. She was skilled at escaping
from enemies. She could hear well, she could see at night,
and her nose would quiver at the slightest breeze.
But she was carrying the little fox, she was tired,
and she was out of breath. Still, on she ran.

At last she smelled it. The stream that ran across the corner
of the farm. She ran until she came to the water,
and then she leaped in. With the kit in her mouth,
she swam to the other side of the stream.
Would the water hide her scent?
Would the dog give up?

Both foxes could hear the dog on the other side
of the stream. It waded in the water, looking for tracks.
It snuffled at the water, searching for the scent.
It ran up and down the bank, looking for its enemy.
It barked at the sun, angry because the fox had
gotten away.
"Where are you, Fox?" it seemed to say.
"Where are you?"

But both foxes were quiet. Both of the foxes lay
under the bushes on the other side of the stream,
hardly breathing. Then the barking grew farther
and farther away.

The vixen began to lick the little fox, and he began
to look for her milk. He drank and she rested.
She had hunted creatures; she had been the hunter.
Now she had become the hunted one.
It was the law of nature, and she knew it.
Once again, she headed home with her kit.

Back in the den, the three kits yipped and yapped
when they saw their mother. They sniffed and snuffed
the little fox, but he smelled just like them.
All four crowded around the vixen, hungry for milk.
They drank their fill, and then they played
the games that all little foxes like to play.

The mother watched them, happy to have her family back
together. The little ones would leave home soon enough.
They would lose their rough, brown coats
and their fur would turn a reddish-brown like hers,
with white bellies and a wonderful, bushy tail.
Their ears and noses would be tipped with black.
Then, in six or seven months, they would leave her
to go off on their own.

Soon, the milk would be gone and she would have to find
other food for them. She would have to find them
beetles and mice to eat. Then, they would be able to hunt
for themselves. What wonderful treats they would find.
Ripe berries, frogs, rats, birds that build their nests
on the ground, and eggs.

The vixen settled the little ones around her,
and they all began to sleep. The sun was still in the sky,
and they felt warm and cozy in the badger hole.
But it wasn't a badger hole any longer.
It was a fox den. It was a home for the four little foxes.

And then, the shadow of a visitor fell over the opening
of the badger hole, of the fox den, of their safe home.

It was the vixen's mate. And he had a large dead rat
in his mouth. A gift for the family.

When they had first met last December,
the two foxes had looked for food together.
Then, in February, everything became very cold.
It was hard to find food. Even the pond in the field
had frozen over. They had to leave the woods
and go to the farm.

They wanted eggs from the chicken house.
It was a cold, dark night.
As soon as the chickens saw the foxes,
they set up a terrible noise. The fox was surprised,
and he grabbed a chicken and killed it.
The two foxes heard the dog, and ran
from the chicken coop.

The mate carried the dead chicken in his mouth.
They made it safely back to the woods where they ate
their catch. They chewed the big feathers
off the bird before they ate the meat.

When the little foxes had been born in April,
the mother had made the den in the badger hole,
but her mate did not live with her. He would bring
her food, once two baby ducklings. Then he would leave
and go back to his own den. He returned often
with food for his mate, because she could not leave
the little ones.

Now he was back with a rat. After the vixen and her mate
had finished their meal, the young kits began to play
with the bones. Their first teeth had started to show
through their gums. They were growing up.
Soon they would be ready to eat solid food.

Later the vixen and her mate left the kits in the den.
They wandered through the woods. The woods were
always full of enemies and the foxes were always on guard.
For a moment the parents were alone.

In a few months, the kits would be grown and they would leave
the vixen to find a new life. This is the way of foxes.

This story tells of a brave animal who risked her life
for her young kit. She protected her young,
and she taught them what they needed to know,
so that one day they too, could take their place
in the circle of nature.

Not all fox stories are pretty ones.
The fox hunts and kills for its life.

When foxes come near humans, trouble often happens.
Sometimes the foxes have rabies and become dangerous
to humans. Sometimes farmers think that a fox
has killed their sheep, and they want to make sure
it doesn't happen again. Sometimes for fun and sport,
people hunt foxes.

Foxes are not pets. They belong to nature.
If a fox is in the city, tell an adult about it
so that the fox can be taken to a safe place.
If you see a fox, leave it alone.

In the circle of nature, man and animals harm
each other. It is sad to think of a bird
that is killed by a fox, or of a fox that is killed
by a farmer or his dog. Animals have to kill
for food or to protect themselves,
and so the circle of nature goes on.

Samuel

by
Bobbi Katz

I found this salamander
Near the pond in the wood.
Samuel, I called him—
Samuel, Samuel.

Right away I loved him.
He loved me too, I think.
Samuel, I called him—
Samuel, Samuel.

I took him home in a coffee can,
And at night
He slept in my bed.
In the morning
I took him to school.

He died very quietly during spelling.

Sometimes I think
I should have left him
Near the pond in the woods.
Samuel, I called him—
Samuel, Samuel.

Doctor Mary's Animals
by
Beverley Allinson and Judith Lawrence

Dr. Mary takes care of animals. She is a veterinarian.
She has cats and dogs, rabbits and birds, lizards
and snakes, gerbils and turtles and many other pets
as patients.

Pets are brought to Dr. Mary's Animal Hospital
by their owners. Some owners carry their pets
in their arms. Some pets come in special boxes.
Some pets don't need to be carried at all.
They can walk in by themselves.

Pets and owners sit in the waiting room
until it is their turn to see Dr. Mary.
Some pets are nervous and would rather be outside.
Others are comfortable and curl up and go to sleep
while they wait. Many of the animals that come
to the hospital can be treated right away.

Some pets have to swallow pills. Others are given injections
to help them recover from an illness. Dr. Mary cleans
and stitches wounds, pulls teeth and cleans ears.
She bathes infected eyes and soothes them with eye drops.
She mends broken legs and sets them in plaster.

Once, Dr. Mary's patient was a poodle that had been hit
by a car. Its back legs were hurt and it couldn't walk.
Dr. Mary knew of a walking carriage
that another veterinarian had invented.
She ordered one for the poodle.

When the carriage was fitted, the poodle was able to wheel
itself along. It wore the walking carriage
until its back legs had mended.

Sometimes an animal needs to have an operation.
Dr. Mary prepares carefully for the operation.
First she scrubs her hands with soap and water.
Then she pulls on rubber gloves and covers
her face with a mask.

When Dr. Mary is ready, the patient is lifted
onto the operating table. Before it has time to be afraid,
it is given an injection that puts it to sleep
until the operation is over.

After an operation, an animal has to stay in hospital
for a few days. Dr. Mary's assistants help her keep
the patients clean and fed. Each patient has its own cage.
Each day the animal's temperature is taken
and it is talked to by Dr. Mary and her assistants.

Not all of the animals in the hospital are recovering
from operations. Some of them have wounds
that can't be bandaged. They have to stay in hospital
until the wounds have healed. Sometimes a cat or dog has
its babies in Dr. Mary's hospital. Then Dr. Mary helps
the mother while its babies are being born.

Half of Dr. Mary's work is at her hospital.
The other half she takes care of from her home.
In the evenings she makes house calls.

One day when she came home from the hospital,
Dr. Mary found that her friend Cory had come to visit.
Cory was swinging in the hammock
with two of Dr. Mary's pets.

"Twiggy and I climbed a tree while we were waiting
for you," Cory told Dr. Mary.
"And now we're having a rest."

"The dogs look as if they're waiting for their turn,"
said Dr. Mary.

"There seem to be more dogs here today
than there were last time," said Cory.

Dr. Mary smiled. "Some of them are just visiting,"
she said. "I never can be sure how many animals
will be here when I get home. Sometimes I have
the feeling that all the dogs in the neighbourhood
drop in for a visit while I'm away."

Cory laughed. "They like coming here as much as I do.
Do you remember the first time I came to visit you?"
she asked.

"I remember very well," said Dr. Mary.
"When I told you about my Animal Hospital,
you laughed and laughed."

"I did too," said Cory, "because I thought you had
animals in little white beds, like the one I was in
when I had my tonsils out."

"A little boy once brought his kitten to my hospital,"
said Dr. Mary. "He expected that the animal doctor
would be a giant cat. He was quite disappointed
when he found it was me."

"That's funny," laughed Cory. "We both made
a funny mistake."

"But now you know what an animal hospital is really like," said Dr. Mary. "You've been to mine lots of times."

"Yes," said Cory, "and I've decided to be a veterinarian too. But I'll have to wait for a few years until I grow up."

"How would you like to practise being an animal doctor with me right now?" asked Dr. Mary. "It's time for me to make my house calls. Will you be my assistant today?"

Cory couldn't believe her ears. Ever since her first visit she had longed to travel with Dr. Mary on her afternoon house calls.

"Now I'll really see some animals," she said.

"What would you like to see?" asked Dr. Mary.

"An elephant," said Cory. "I'd definitely like to see something as big as an elephant."

Before they left her house, Dr. Mary wrote down the names and addresses of the owners who had phoned her that day.

"Many pet owners ask me to call at their homes," she told Cory. "And sometimes I go to the place where the owner works."

"Where are we going first?" asked Cory, as she and Dr. Mary got into the car.

"To see Don's two dogs. He has them with him at his shop."

"Are the dogs sick?" asked Cory.

"Not anymore, I hope," said Dr. Mary. "One of them had a sore ear but it should be better by now. Don called because it's time both his dogs had their rabies shots."

Don and his dogs were waiting outside his shop when Cory and Dr. Mary arrived. Dr. Mary checked Blackie's ear. Dr. Mary didn't seem to mind that Blackie poked out her tongue and rolled her eyes.

"She looks the way I feel when I'm scared," laughed Cory.

"She hasn't anything to worry about," said Dr. Mary. "Her ear is quite better."

"I'll hold them while you give them their shots," said Don.

Cory watched as Dr. Mary took a needle from her black bag. She fitted a tube of liquid onto the needle and gave Blackie her shot. Then she used another needle for Goldie.

"There," said Dr. Mary. "That should take care of them for another year."

"Thanks, Doctor," said Don. "Do you want me to pay you now?"

"I'll send you my account in the mail," said Dr. Mary. "Come on, Cory, we have some more calls to make."

Dr. Mary and Cory drove for a while until they reached Tony's home. He had phoned Dr. Mary because his kitten had a bad cough.

"He hasn't been eating much," Tony told Dr. Mary. "So I thought you should see him before it developed into something more serious."

"Hmmm," said Dr. Mary. "He has a slight temperature. I'll give him an injection and leave you some pills to give him. Call me on Thursday if he isn't any better."

"More injections," said Cory.

"Yes, but for different reasons," said Dr. Mary. "This one is to make the kitten better. The others were to keep the dogs well."

"What's that? What's that?" croaked a strange voice.

"What's that?" said Cory.

Dr. Mary and Tony laughed. "That's Peppy," said Tony.
"Come and meet him."

Peppy was a big brightly coloured parrot. "He's a macaw,"
said Dr. Mary.

"I have some smaller parrots," said Tony.
"They're very friendly too."

The small parrots were cockatiels. They were so tame
they flew around the house. One perched on Cory's arm.
Another landed on Dr. Mary's head.

The last call of the day was a surprise for Cory.
They went to visit Finn McCool, who was a special friend
of Dr. Mary's.

"I thought you might like to meet Finn," said Dr. Mary.
"What do you think of him?"

"He's not as big as an elephant," said Cory.
"But he's the biggest dog I've ever seen."

"He's an Irish wolfhound," said Dr. Mary. "I've known him
ever since he was a puppy. He's always glad to see me
and sorry when I leave."

"I'm sorry this is our last call," said Cory.
"This has been the best day of my life."

"We'll spend another day together," said Dr. Mary.
"And we'll come and visit Finn again."

"Come back soon," said Finn McCool.

My Dog

by
Bernice Aylen

When thunder splits the sky
And lightning quivers at the window
My dog crawls behind the sofa.

He covers his ears with his paws
and whimpers.

I'm not really afraid
But my dog needs company.
So I crawl in beside him
And cuddle up
Close.

A Bumpy Ride for a Bear

by

Shirley Benton Kerr

"Dad! Dad!" I called. "There's a bear down by the barn."

Dad pushed back his cap, shook his head, and muttered.
I couldn't hear what he said,
but it was probably something like,
"What an imagination!"

He yelled, "Get on with your chores. There hasn't been
a bear around these parts for twenty years or more."

I knew there was no use arguing with him so I ran
to the house and shouted, "Mom! There's a bear
down by the barn."

Mom called out the door, "Really, Jason?
Well bring him in for some honey buns."

I could hear her chuckle.

I went right into the house and said, "Mom,
there really is a bear down by the barn.
I mean it."

Mom scolded. "This is too much, Jason. I don't mind
you having an active imagination, but you have to know
when to stop pretending."

"Please come down by the barn, Mom," I pleaded.
"I'm not imagining anything. There is a bear there.
Honest!"

I walked slowly out of the house, hoping
she would call me back; she didn't of course.
She remembered too many other times I guess.
Like when my "ghost" down in the cornfield
was one of her sheets that had blown off the clothes-line.

I saw Dad heading for the barn.
"He must have believed me, after all," I thought.
I ran to meet him.

"The bear must have gone inside the barn," I said.

"Are you still on about that bear?" Dad asked.
He walked over to the tractor that was parked
beside the barn. He climbed up, and started it.
The noise of the tractor must have made
the bear curious, because he poked his head
out of the barn door.

"There he is," I shouted.

Dad looked where I was pointing and saw the bear.
"My stars!" he exclaimed.
"There really is a bear."

He pushed back his cap and scratched his head.
That always means he is really puzzled.
"Now, what do you know about that?"

"What are you going to do?" I asked.

Dad climbed down from the tractor.
"We'll go around to the back of the barn
and bang on it," he said. "That might scare him
out of the barn."

But as we rounded the first corner of the barn,
the bear walked out of the barn and climbed up
on the tractor. He was so big that he hit
some of the controls as he climbed in.

The tractor took off across the farm
with a very bewildered bear sitting on it,
and Dad and I started after it, not believing our eyes.
With nobody steering it, the tractor went over anything
that was in the way. This made a very bumpy ride for the bear.

"What can we do?" I asked Dad.

"There's not much we can do," Dad answered.
"We'll just have to hope it runs out of gas soon."

We trudged along, trying to follow the sound.

"I think he's in the meadow," Dad said. "At least
he can't come to much harm there. Thank goodness
the tractor wasn't heading for the highway."

I said, "I can see why you say the tractor
should never be left running."

"Well," Dad answered, "I never expected a bear to take off
in it, but that shows you never can tell what will happen."
He stopped walking and listened.
The noise of the tractor had stopped.
"Something has happened!" Dad cried.
"That tractor couldn't have run out of gas yet. Come on."
We both raced to the meadow.

What we saw when we got there made us smile
in spite of ourselves. The tractor had hit a small tree
on the edge of the meadow, and stalled.

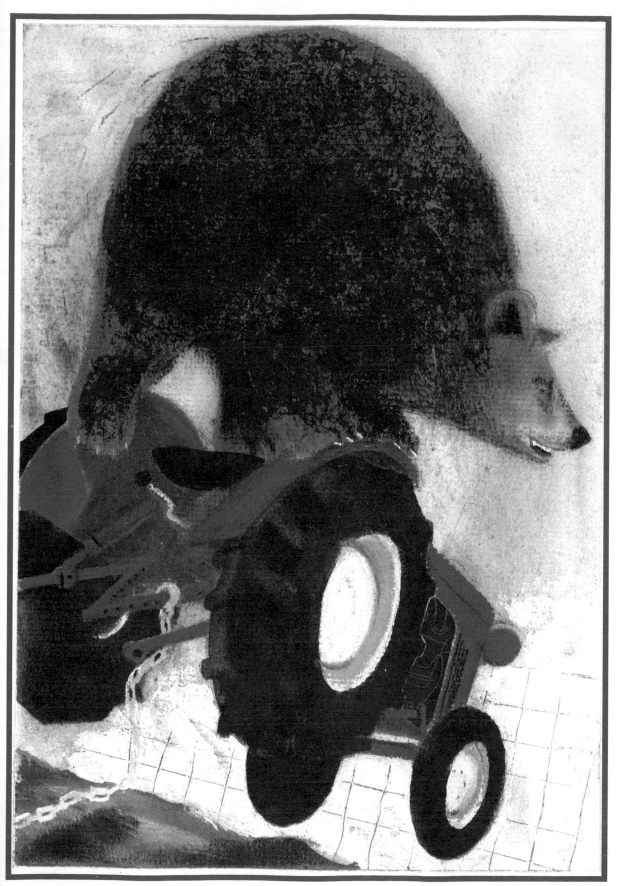

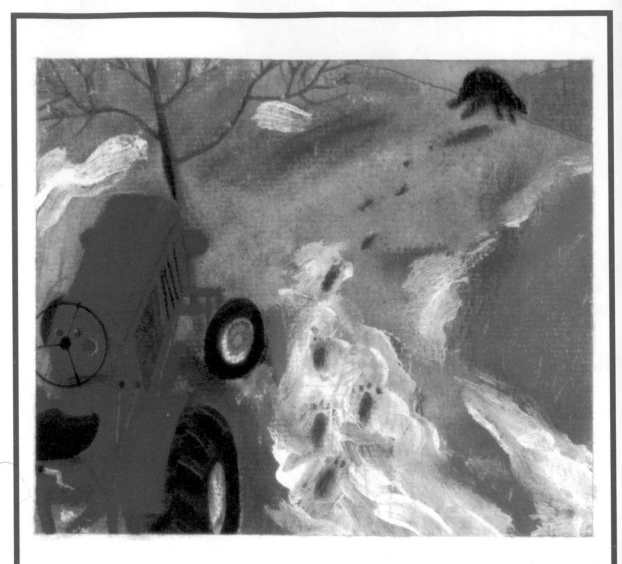

The bear was stunned, but unhurt.
He climbed down from the tractor,
and when his feet were on the ground
he took off in great haste across the meadow
to the woods.

Dad took off his cap, scratched his head, and said,
"Somehow, I don't think we'll see a bear around these parts
for another twenty years."

I felt rather sorry about that.

Pooh's Alphabet Book
by
A.A. Milne

Animal

"It is hard to be brave," said Piglet, sniffing slightly,
"when you're only a Very Small **Animal**."

Bear

"I am a **Bear** of Very Little Brain,
and long words Bother me."

Christopher Robin

"I've got two names," said **Christopher Robin** carelessly.

Day

"Many happy returns of the **day**," said Piglet.

"Meaning me?"

"Of course, Eeyore."

"My birthday?"

"Yes."

"Me having a real birthday?"

"Yes, Eeyore, and I've brought you a present."

Eat

And then, suddenly, he remembered. He had **eaten** Eeyore's birthday present!

Friend

"Eeyore," he said solemnly, "I, Winnie-the-Pooh, will find your tail for you."

"Thank you, Pooh," answered Eeyore.
"You're a real **friend**," said he.
"Not like Some," he said.

Grandfather

Pooh was wondering what a **Grandfather** was like,
and if perhaps this was Two Grandfathers
they were after now, and, if so,
whether he would be allowed
to take one home and keep it.

Honey

"I just like to know," said Pooh humbly.
"So as I can say to myself: I've got fourteen pots
of **honey** left. Or fifteen, as the case may be.
It's sort of comforting."

Idea

There was a moment's silence while everybody thought.
"I've got a sort of **idea**," said Pooh at last,
"but I don't suppose it's a very good one."

"I don't suppose it is either," said Eeyore.

Jagular

The **Jagular** called out to them. "Help! Help!" it called.

"That's what Jagulars always do," said Pooh,
much interested. "They call 'Help! Help!'
and then when you look up, they drop on you."

"I'm looking down," cried Piglet loudly,
so as the **Jagular** shouldn't do
the wrong thing by accident.

Kanga

"Don't open the mouth, dear, or the soap goes in,"
said **Kanga.** "There! What did I tell you?"

"You—you—you did it on purpose,"
spluttered Piglet.

Love

"Oh, Bear!" said Christopher Robin,
"How I do **love** you!"

"So do I," said Pooh.

Mistake

Christopher Robin went back to lunch with his friends
Pooh and Piglet, and on the way they told him
of the Awful **Mistake** they had made.
And when he had finished laughing, they all sang
the Outdoor Song for Snowy Weather
the rest of the way home.

Noise

"What can it be?" Pooh thought. "There are lots of noises
in the Forest, but this is a different one. It isn't a growl,
and it isn't a purr, and it isn't a bark, and it isn't
the **noise**-you-make-before-beginning-a-piece-of-poetry,
but it's a **noise** of some kind, made by a strange animal.
And he's making it outside my door. So I shall get up
and ask him not to do it."

Owl

"And if anyone knows anything about anything," said Bear to himself, "it's **Owl** who knows something about something," he said, "or my name's not Winnie-the-Pooh," he said. "Which it is," he added. "So there you are."

Pooh and Piglet

Piglet sidled up to **Pooh** from behind.
"**Pooh**!" he whispered.

"Yes, **Piglet**?"

"Nothing," said **Piglet**, taking Pooh's paw.
"I just wanted to be sure of you."

Queen Bee

"We must be practical. The important bee to deceive is the **Queen Bee**. Can you see which is the **Queen Bee** from down there?"

"No."

Rabbit

"**Rabbit**," said Pooh to himself, "I like talking to **Rabbit**. He talks about sensible things. He doesn't use long, difficult words, like Owl. He uses short, easy words, like 'What about lunch?' and 'Help yourself, Pooh.' I suppose, really, I ought to go and see **Rabbit**."

Spelling

"My **spelling** is Wobbly. It's good **spelling** but it Wobbles, and the letters get in the wrong places."

Tigger

"All I did was I coughed," said **Tigger**.

"He bounced," said Eeyore.

"Well, I sort of boffed," said **Tigger**.

"Hush!" said Rabbit, holding up his paw. "What does Christopher Robin think about it all? That's the point."

Useful

"Well, it's a very nice pot, even if there's no honey in it, and if I washed it clean, and got somebody to write 'A Happy Birthday' on it, Eeyore could keep things in it, which might be **Useful**."

Verse

"This is the first **verse**," Pooh said to Piglet.

"First **verse** of what?"

"My song."

"What song?"

"This one."

"Which one?"

"Well if you listen, Piglet, you'll hear it."

"How do you know I'm not listening?"

Winnie-the-Pooh

"He's **Winnie-ther-Pooh**. Don't you know what *'ther'* means?"

"Ah, yes, now I do," I said quickly; and I hope you do too, because it is all the explanation you are going to get.

Expotition

"We are all going on an Expedition," said Christopher Robin.

"Going on an **Expotition**?" said Pooh eagerly, "I don't think I've ever been on one of those. Where are we going to on this **Expotition?**"

"Expedition, silly old Bear. It's got an 'x' in it."

"Oh!" said Pooh. "I know." But he didn't really.

Yesterday

"I think," said Piglet, when he licked the tip of his nose too, and found that it brought very little comfort, "I think that I have just remembered something that I forgot to do **yesterday** and shan't be able to do tomorrow. So I suppose I really ought to go back and do it now."

Buzz

"That **buzzing**-noise means something. You don't get a **buzzing**-noise like that, just **buzzing** and **buzzing**, without its meaning something. If there's a **buzzing**-noise, somebody's making a **buzzing**-noise, and the only reason for making a **buzzing**-noise that I know of is because you're a bee."

Stamp Collecting
by
Vincent Wong

People collect anything, from bottle caps to old money.
I prefer to collect stamps. People collect stamps
because they can be worth a lot of money, but I collect
stamps for the pictures on them.

You can learn a lot from stamps, too.
If the space shuttle landed on another planet,
you might learn about it from the picture on a stamp.
Sometimes when important or famous people die,
like Terry Fox, their pictures are put on stamps.

Commemorative stamps are stamps that remind people of things,
like one hundred year anniversaries, or important events
of the past. There are commemorative stamps
for the Montreal Olympics. I have also learned
about old airplanes and boats from stamps.

If you decide to start a collection, you can get started in different ways. I got started because there were a lot of stamps lying around my house. I put them in a small album, and there I was—a small collector!

You can also get stamps from your friends. Ask them to save all the stamps they get on letters mailed to their house. If anyone you know is going away on a holiday, ask him or her to mail you a letter. In this way you can get stamps from all around the world.

You will need a stamp album. If you are going to buy one with pictures of stamps printed on the pages, make sure the pictures are of modern stamps, as you are not likely to find a 1940 stamp on a letter these days.

When you are taking a stamp from an envelope, first cut
around the stamp, making sure you don't cut the stamp.
Soak it in water for about ten minutes, then go back
and peel the stamp off the envelope. If it doesn't come off
easily, let it soak for a little while longer.
You should never pick up a stamp with your fingers,
as you might damage or dirty it; always use
a pair of tweezers.

To put the stamp in the album, use a stamp hinge.
This is a small piece of gummed paper. You lick the hinge,
and stick one fold on the stamp and the other in the album.
This does not damage the stamp, and it can be easily removed
if you want to trade it.

If you are going to be a serious stamp collector,
there are some words you should know.
A *cancelled stamp* is one that has been used
to mail a letter. It has the post office stamp
on it. This is called the *postmark*.

Some stamps are worth more if they have been cancelled.
Some cancellations also have the date on them, so you know
when the stamp was used. If a stamp is brand new,
it is called in *mint condition*. A *first day cover* is a letter
posted on the first day a new stamp is on sale.

If you want to buy stamps from a dealer, you can send away
for approvals. You will see advertisements for these in
newspapers and stamp magazines. When you get them,
keep the ones you want and send back the other stamps,
and the money.

There are many different kinds of stamps,
and many different kinds of collectors.
Some people might want to collect only stamps
from the year 1900. They are not likely to find many,
but it's just a thought. If you become a collector,
you will find you have lots of friends.

Stamps of Canada

Terry Fox

Expo 1967

Montreal
Olympics 1976

Military Aircraft

Inland Boats

Military Aircraft

The Three Penny Beaver

Fathers
of Confederation

The Bluenose

RCMP Centennial Stamp

Queen Elizabeth II

1983 Stamp

The Collection
by
Meguido Zola

Bubblegum cards in my pocket...
Bubblegum cards in my lunch pail...
Bubblegum cards in my desk...
Bubblegum cards in my jacket...
Bubblegum cards in my gym bag...
Bubblegum cards in my hat...
Bubblegum cards in my toy box...
Bubblegum cards in my brain!

Sally Can't See
by
Palle Petersen

Two girls are walking together in the sunshine.
Sally's hair is long and dark and Pat's is short
and fair. Pat isn't as tall as Sally
though both girls are twelve years old.

Both can hear the birds and smell the flowers,
feel the hot sun on their faces and the hard path
under their feet. And Pat looks at everything
around her.

But Sally can't see.

Sally knows when the sun is shining—she can feel
its warmth. But for her there is one sense missing.
Usually we have five senses—we can see, hear, feel,
smell and taste.

Although Sally can't see, she can feel the shape
and softness of the flowers and the dustiness
of the dry earth and she can hear the bees buzzing,
so she knows it is a summer's day.

She is quite used to what we call darkness
because she was born blind.

This is what Sally sees.

We call this colour black
and this is what it is like for Sally
whether the sun is shining
or the moon is bright.

Close your eyes tight and cover them with your hands.
Then you will see all that Sally can see.

Because of her blindness Sally goes to a special school.
She doesn't go home at the end of each day. Instead,
she sleeps at school every night until the end of term
when her mother and father come to take her home
for the holidays.

It is important for all children to learn to take care
of themselves. But it is especially important for Sally
and her teachers help her in all kinds of ways.

In school, Sally works hard at finding out the shapes
of things and she runs her fingers carefully
over every object.

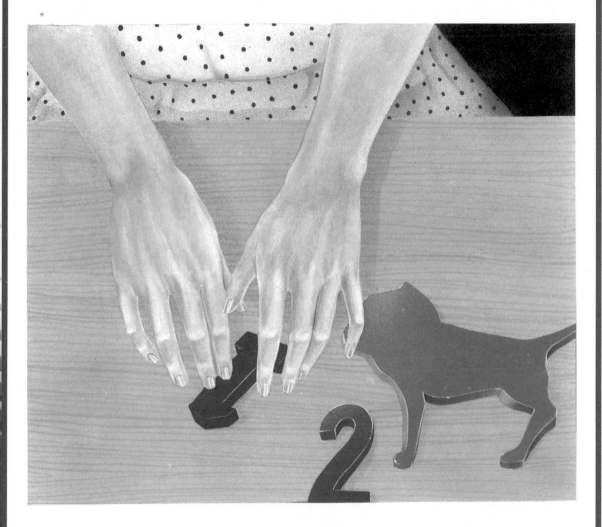

Instead of having pictures to look at,
Sally has shapes to feel. She has learned to remember
with her finger tips and knows a lion or a number
or even the shape of a country.

And Sally learns and remembers with her fingers.

In her twelve years, Sally has learned a lot about sounds.
The different sounds of people's feet and voices,
the banging of doors and the clatter of dishes in the sink.

With other children she has a lot of fun learning
about music and the sounds it makes.
The thud, thud, thud of a drum,
the high sweet tones of a recorder
and the tinkle of a tambourine.

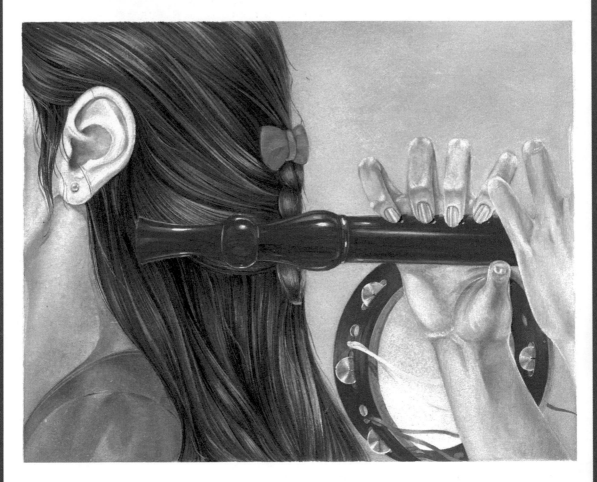

And Sally learns and remembers with her ears.

But it takes longer when you are blind, and you have to learn
to be patient.

Because Sally can't see it took her a long time
to learn to read and write but she managed it.
And this is because of Braille writing.

Braille is a way of making letters with bumps
that you can feel because they stick up on the page.
The bumps make patterns and Sally has had to learn
the patterns with her finger tips and remember them.

Now Sally reads a lot of Braille books and enjoys
the stories.

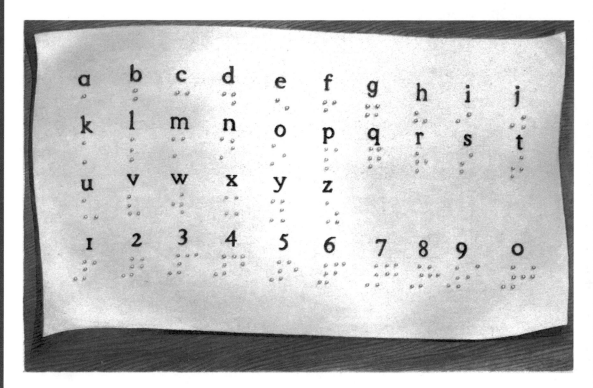

Here are the shapes used in Braille for the letters
of the alphabet and numbers.

And she has learned to type and writes letters home
on a typewriter. But if anyone sends her a letter
or a card a sighted person has to read it to her.

Imagine swimming when you can't see!
But Sally has learned not to be afraid of the water
and if she knocks into someone, she laughs
and pushes herself away and swims on.

But there is always a grown-up close by who can watch
and help Sally and the other blind children
if they need it.

When Sally was learning to jump, she started with the rope
close to the ground. But now the rope is quite high
and she feels for its height with her fingers
before she jumps. And there is a big pit of soft sand
to land on which makes Sally feel safe.

And always the teacher is close at hand.

Best of all, Sally likes the days when she has riding lessons.
She always has the same horse called Prince
who is gentle and steady. But a sighted person keeps
close at hand to help Sally to be confident
and sure of herself.

Because of her riding, Sally has learned a great deal
about her horse. She knows about his shape and size,
the feel of his coat, and how he stands
on his four strong legs.

So she has been able to help to make a model of a horse
in the classroom. Some of the children are not
completely blind and this helps when they are
all working together.

When she is at home for the holidays, Sally likes to go shopping on her own. But she can only go along the streets she knows well, using her long white cane to feel the way.

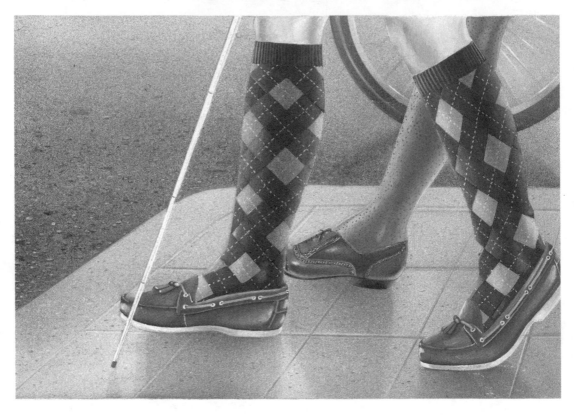

As she steps forward with her right foot, she swings her cane to the left because the cane has to feel for the place where her left foot is going to tread. This way Sally can be sure there is nothing to stumble over. Her white stick shows other people that she is blind and it helps her to find the curb or feel for a lamp-post or a step.

And all the time, Sally listens. She can hear the cars but she is still afraid of bicycles which move so quietly and are difficult to hear.

At home she knows exactly where every bit of furniture is.
Her mother is careful never to put anything, even a chair,
in a different place.

Sally likes playing the organ. She learns the notes
from music written in Braille. She feels the bumps
with her left hand and plays the song with her right.

Pip is Sally's budgie. She has taught him to talk
and she cleans out his cage every day.

Pip often flies around the room,
then comes to land on Sally's finger or her head.
They are good friends and at holiday times
they spend many hours together.

Sally has learned a lot about this little bird
by using her ears and fingers.

Nearly every summer Sally goes to the beach with her mother and father and she loves to swim and play in the water.

But sometimes she meets strangers who are sorry for her because she is blind. This makes Sally upset and angry because these people seem to think there is something strange about her. And all she wants is to be treated as much like other children as possible.

So if you ever meet a blind person, remember Sally who everyday is learning so much although she cannot see.

Wishers
by
Dolores Hind

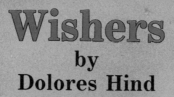

Take a dandelion fluffy and gray.
Gently blow the puff away,
And wish a wish.

Take a milkweed with soft, white hair.
Gently blow each strand in the air,
And wish a wish.

Meet the Beetles

by
Owl Magazine

Watch out—these beetles crawling towards you
are ferocious hunters! Fortunately, unless you are
smaller than a pea—you're in no danger. In fact,
if you are bigger than a pea, you can discover
that beetles are beautiful to look at...

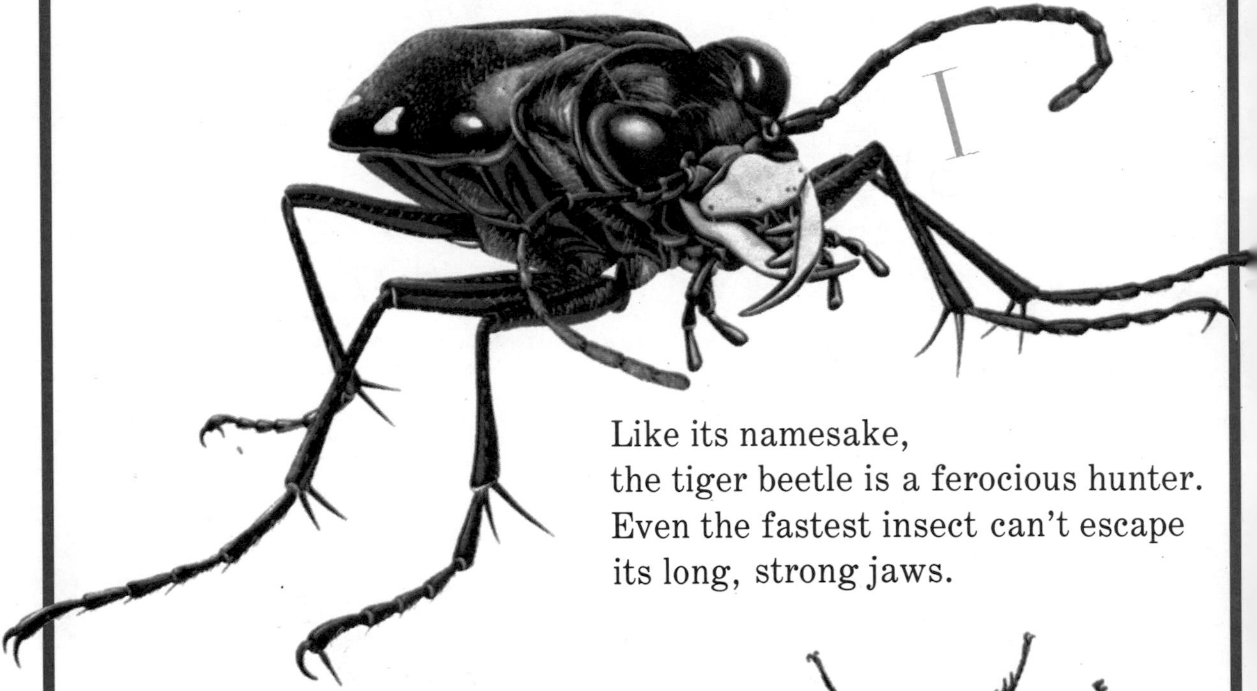

Like its namesake,
the tiger beetle is a ferocious hunter.
Even the fastest insect can't escape
its long, strong jaws.

Male stag beetles have
huge jaws that are branched
like antlers. They use them
as weapons when they fight
a battle.

*The actual sizes of the beetles are shown by this sign ├──────┤

If you were as strong
as this stag beetle,
you could pick up
and walk off
with a small car.

This ground beetle smells
and tastes so horrible
that even the hungriest toad
or bird will immediately
drop it.

The bright colours
of the milkweed leaf beetle
warn enemies to stay away.
Good thing, too,
because this beetle feeds on
the poisonous milkweed plant.

When it's frightened,
the flea beetle
springs into action
by using its
muscular back legs
to bound
through the air.

When the weevil
is frightened,
it folds up its legs
and plays dead.

How does the long-horned
twig borer beetle smell?
With its very long antennae,
of course.

This ground beetle hunts
only at night.
During the day it snoozes
under rocks,
logs or leaves.

Depending on how the sun
shines on this leaf beetle,
it can look either green or gold.
That's because it has
a very thin layer of armour
on its back that acts like a prism
to break up the sunlight.

Unlike other beetles,
this ground beetle has
no wings under its back plates.
Instead, its plates are welded
together to form a strong shield.

Tiger beetles come
in different sizes
and colours.
But no matter
what they look like,
they're all fierce hunters.

Hey, Bug!
by
Lilian Moore

Hey, bug, stay!
Don't run away.
I know a game that we can play.

I'll hold my fingers very still
and you can climb a finger-hill.

No, no.
Don't go.

Here's a wall—a tower, too,
a tiny bug town, just for you.
I've a cookie. You have some.
Take this oatmeal cookie crumb.

Hey, bug, stay!
Hey, bug!
Hey!

No Matter
by
Lee Bennett Hopkins

No matter
how hot-burning
it is
outside

when

you peel a
long, fat cucumber

or

cut deep into
a fresh, ripe watermelon

you can
feel
coolness
come into your hands.

One Red Tomato
by
Roger Aske

It all happened the summer Dad decided to give up baseball.
He had been the coach of the Pee Wee Royals
for seven years.

"I've had enough," he said at the supper table one night.
"I've had enough."

He had just been talking to the manager of the team
for almost an hour. I could tell by the way he slammed down
the telephone that it had made him feel ugly.
Big people are like that sometimes—they get ugly
about baseball games. It doesn't matter whether
they are big league games or little league games
they still get ugly.

"What are you going to do all summer?" my mother wanted
to know.

"Relax," Dad said.

"You will be bored to tears," my mother said.

"I'm going to grow vegetables," Dad said.

"Oh dear," Mother exclaimed. "Do we have enough room?"

"We have enough," Dad said.

Nobody believed him of course, but on the first day
of baseball it was mother who drove me to the park
and not Dad. I knew something was going to change.

When I came home Dad had dug up a square patch of ground
in the middle of the backyard. I thought it looked
kind of neat. Mother wasn't saying anything.
She was pretending to do things at the kitchen sink
while she watched out the window.

"What is he going to grow, Mom?" I asked her.

"Everything, I think," she sighed.

Dad bought packets of seeds at the garden shop.
He read all the instructions on the back of the packets
several times and then he stared at the pictures
of the vegetables on the front. I think he was wondering
how the vegetables would grow without a lot of coaching
from him. Dad likes to talk and explain things. He likes
to tell everyone how he wants things done.

He planted the seeds in thin rows, kneeling on the ground;
his glasses slipped off the end of his nose. He got mad
at the carrot seeds because they were so small.
But when he had finished he wrote out a notice
and stuck it in one corner of the garden.
It said: PLEASE KEEP OFF THE INFIELD.
It was Dad's joke but it made me feel sad.

Then one day, on his way home from work, he bought a box
of tomato plants. "Look," he said to mother as he carried
them into the house.

"Tomatoes?" my mother said although she knew what they were.

"The man at the shop said they would be red and beautiful
and as big as baseballs," Dad said.

Mother didn't say anything but she had a look on her face
which wasn't so sure.

Every morning before breakfast Dad was out there watching.
He stood very still, staring down at the garden,
looking for the first crack in the soil,
looking for the first seedling to break through.
The radishes came first, and then the lettuce,
and then the carrots. It was easy to tell something
new had happened in the garden because when Dad sat down
to breakfast his smile was as wide as a slice of melon.

It was the tomatoes which upset the summer.
When they had yellow blossoms they were exciting.
Then the blossoms became tiny green fruit
and that was more exciting. The green fruit got bigger
and rounder every day. They weren't as big as baseballs
but that didn't matter. Everyone was waiting
for them to turn red.

Dad started to worry about the sun.
The sun was never out long enough and never strong enough
for Dad. When the clouds covered it up Dad's slice-of-melon
smile disappeared until the sun came out again.

One morning I was just getting out of bed when I heard Dad
calling Mother out into the garden. I ran out to see
what had happened. Mother was standing with her arm
around Dad's shoulders and they were gazing down
at the first red tomato.

"It's beautiful," my mother said.

"Wow! You did it, Dad," I added.

Dad's slice-of-melon smile was back.

One day Dad was working and Mother had gone shopping
and I was left with an empty morning. I wandered over
to the garden to see if there were any more red tomatoes.
There was only the one and it really looked beautiful.
It had a fresh good-to-eat look. Really nice.

Anyway I touched it and it sort of fell into my hand.
And then I ate it. It was a funny thing to do
because I don't like tomatoes very much.

Mom came home and blamed the neighbour's kids. Dad said
it was the crows. He said he was going to do something
about it.

"What can you do?" Mother wanted to know.

"I'll build a scarecrow," Dad said.

I wanted to help him but I didn't. I felt terrible.
Dad made the scarecrow with sticks and a pole
and an old shopping basket for a head. He dressed it
like a baseball player in a pair of striped pants,
a shirt with someone's name torn off the back,
and a greasy green cap.

As a last touch he stuck an old baseball mitt on the end
of one arm. The scarecrow looked silly. It looked
like a kid who had given up on a fly ball because he knew
he was going to miss it. Every time I looked
at the scarecrow I felt terrible.

Perhaps the scarecrow would have protected
the next red tomato. At least it would have reminded me
not to eat it. But then it began to rain.
Every day it rained. If it didn't rain it looked
as if it was going to rain. All the tomatoes stayed
as green as the grass around the edge of the garden.

Dad was getting bored. Sometimes he didn't bother
to go out before breakfast anymore. The carrots
and the lettuce and the radishes were all terrific
but they didn't seem to count. Dad wanted red tomatoes.

"Maybe we should make pickles out of them
if they are only going to be green," my mother suggested.

"Never," Dad said, and that was that.

I expected to see him sneaking back to the ball games,
and once I missed a play because I thought I saw him
in the crowd near the backstop. I was hoping
he would come back because he wasn't happy
with the vegetable garden anymore.

One day in September after we had lost the second game
of the final series I wandered around to the back
of the house without going inside because I didn't want
to tell Dad I had struck out three times.
But he was right there at the edge of the garden.
There was a small heap of green tomatoes
at this feet and he had a baseball bat in his hand.
Every few seconds, he picked one up,
threw it into the air and swung at it.
He was aiming right at the scarecrow.

"Striiiike," he shouted every time he missed one,
but he didn't miss often. Most of them were spattered
all over the shirt and the basket-head of the scarecrow.
"You see," he said when he saw me watching.
"You see you've got to follow through with the bat. Watch."
The next green tomato went clear over the roof of the house.

Anyway, that was last summer.
This summer mother is looking after the vegetable garden
and Dad is back coaching the Pee Wee Royals.
One of these days after we have had a good game
I might tell him who stole that one red tomato.

Cat
by
Mary Britton Miller

The black cat yawns,
Opens her jaws,
Stretches her legs,
And shows her claws.

Then she gets up
And stands on four
Long, stiff legs
And yawns some more.

She shows her sharp teeth,
She stretches her lip,
Her slice of a tongue
Turns up at the tip.

Lifting herself
On her delicate toes,
She arches her back
As high as it goes.

She lets herself down
With particular care,
And pads away
With her tail in the air.

What for You So Crazy?
by
Roger Aske

My name is Francine and I am eight years old.
On the twenty-third of July last year I got stuck
on the roof. Stuck is not the right word
because I wasn't stuck like scotch-tape to brown paper.
I just couldn't get down. My mother says I was silly
to go up there but I had to help Sample.

Sample is a cat. He lives with us in our bungalow
at 17 Green Street. When he was a very small kitten,
the manager of the super-market put him in a carton
and gave him to my mother. "Keep him," the manager
said to my mother with a big smile. "He's free."

"Oh no," said my mother, but it was too late.
I already had him in my arms and was running
through the parking lot and back to the car.

In those days he was a ball of fur and tiny bones
and I loved him very much. Dad called him Sample
because he was a little something which we got
for nothing.

Sample was a nice, soft name for a kitten. But when he grew
into a fierce, ginger cat with a torn ear and a black patch
around one eye, most people called him Sam.
I still love him, even when he is called Sam,
but some people don't. Some people hate cats.
Mister Livorno hates cats.

Mister Livorno is a painter who came to change the colour
of our house. He drives a bright, blue and yellow truck
with LIVORNO THE PAINTER in big letters on each side.
Mister Livorno is a very happy man and he sings
all the time. When he arrived he walked all around
the garden admiring the flowers and singing a song
about the beautiful day. He sang even when he was standing
on his ladder slapping on the paint with a big brush.

"Yoo Hoo la la, la la, la ley."

I didn't really mind it because the song seemed to float
away in the air, but Sample didn't like it. He lay
in the short grass with one paw rubbing at his ear
and his tail twitching angrily.

"Yoo Hoo la la, la la, la ley."

The trouble began because Sample and Mister Livorno
both like birds. Sample likes to eat them.
There is nothing wrong with that. Dad says that cats eat birds
and birds eat worms and that is the way it is. I don't know
what worms eat but they must be very busy digging holes.

Mister Livorno liked to listen to the birds. When he heard them singing he even stopped singing himself. "Bello," he said. "So beautiful." And he would hold his paintbrush in the air for a long time before he started to work again.

"Yoo Hoo la la, la la, la ley."

On the twenty-third of July Mister Livorno was painting the front of the house. The sun was shining and the sky was blue and I was sitting on the doorstep reading a book about bears. Suddenly a big robin came winging out of the spruce trees at the back of the house and landed on the lawn.

It landed halfway between the bottom
of Mister Livorno's ladder and Sample's whiskers.

Mister Livorno must have seen it because he stopped
singing. Sample saw it because his eyes squeezed together
and he set his paws like a tiger. I don't think
the robin saw anything. It hopped one hop.
Mister Livorno turned and looked down.
Sample twitched his torn ear and laid
his tail very flat. The robin hopped another hop.

Mister Livorno started to climb down the ladder.
Sample crawled and crouched. The robin twisted
his head and peered at the ground with one eye.

"Via!" said Mister Livorno as he almost bounced off
the bottom of the ladder. "Scram!"
Sample leaped and missed as the robin squawked
and flapped its wings and flew back into the spruce trees.

But that wasn't enough for Mister Livorno.
"Scat!" he shouted, waving his brush at Sample
as if he was going to paint him the same colour
as the house. Sample didn't wait.
He jumped and twisted in the air and took off
as fast as he could. Mister Livorno followed.

"Via! Via!" he shouted several times.
Around the house they went once; around the house
they went twice. Sample ran and stopped
and ran again. Mister Livorno huffed and puffed.
His big stomach was shaking and his face
was getting redder and redder.

When Sample came around the corner for the second time
and clawed his way up the ladder and onto the roof
I knew he was safe. Perhaps Mister Livorno knew
Sample was safe too. He was so out of breath
and so upset that he gave up.

"Cats. I hate cats," he roared, and he dumped
his paint brush into the pot hanging on the ladder
and he climbed into his blue and yellow truck
and he drove away.

"Oh dear," I said to myself wondering how I was going
to explain it all to mother. "Trouble," I said to myself.
Then I heard Sample. He was sitting at the very top
of the roof crying like a baby.

"Sample," I said softly but firmly.
"Come down Sample. Sample, come down."
But Sample wouldn't hear of it.

I doubt if he could hear anything but his own crying.
I really thought he was being stupid
because it looked very easy to come down.
"Sample," I pleaded. "Sample,
please come down."

He tried. He put his front paws on the downward slope
and then took them away. He turned around
and did the same thing on the other side.
It was no use. He turned to look down at me
and opened his mouth and cried even louder.

"All right, all right," I said. "I'm coming."
And when I think how I went up that ladder
and all the way up the roof it scares me
because it was so easy.
"Wow," I said when I reached the top.
"Oh wow," I said and then sat down
very quickly.

Sample didn't even come over to say "Thank you."
When he saw me come up to the top, he just strolled
down the roof and disappeared over the edge.
So it wasn't Sample who was stuck,
it was me.

There was no way I was going down. After all,
I didn't have four feet full of claws; just two feet
in old sneakers. I hardly dared to move my head.
"Oh wow," I said. "Trouble," I said.

The view was amazing although I didn't think so
at the time. I could see over the top
of Mrs. Wilkinson's house and all the way to the river.

I could see up the street and down the street.
I could see Mr. Yablonski's washing hanging on the line
and I could see Sandy MacLean cutting the lawn.
I think I could have seen the whole world
if I'd really looked, but I wasn't looking.

"Help," I said in a very little voice because I really didn't want
anyone to know I was there. "Help," I said in a bigger voice
because I thought someone should know I was there. "Help."
I did hear a little voice answer me from somewhere
and when I dared to look down it was Sample,
sitting on the grass, looking up at me.
It was so silly it made me want to cry.

Then, as suddenly as Mister Livorno had driven away,
he came back. I think he saw me before he turned
into the driveway because his blue and yellow truck
nearly went off the road into Mrs. Wilkinson's garden.

"So help me to believe it," he said as he jumped
out of the cab. "You crazy or something else?"
he shouted up to me.

"I'm stuck," I said.

"Then you stay stuck right there," he shouted.
"Don't you move one finger, not even one thumb."

"Oh help," I cried, wondering if my fingers and thumbs
were going to move. I felt really terrible.

I heard Mister Livorno puffing up the ladder
and then he walked up the roof as if it was a level road.
He put one of his strong arms around me and hugged me
to his stomach until I thought I was squashed.
When we reached the bottom of the ladder he lifted me
in his hands and kissed my cheek with his big, bushy moustache.

"What for you so crazy?" he asked.

"I was trying to help Sample," I said.

"Sample? What is this Sample?" he wanted to know
as he put me down and wiped his forehead
with a large red hankerchief.

"Sample is our cat, Mister Livorno," I said.

"Cat?" said Mister Livorno angrily. "I hate cats."
His face started to go very red again so I didn't say
anything.

I could see Sample sneaking away through the bushes
at the edge of the road so I knew he was safe.
But I didn't really feel better until Mister Livorno
started singing again.

"Yoo Hoo la la, la la, la ley."

At Grandmother's House

by
John Lim

Grandma

When Johnnie was a little boy he lived with his parents
in the city of Singapore on the island of Singapore. Every Friday
afternoon his father drove him, his mother, his older brother
and sister—and sometimes his aunt and cousins—
out to the country to spend the weekend with his grandmother.

Grandmother lived in a tiny house in an orchard
of fruit trees and flower bushes. The house was built
of wood and had a thatched straw roof. In the front
was a veranda where Grandma sat in the evening. She lived
all alone with a dog called Jackie and a cat called Cat.

Grandma and Grandpa had come down from China to live
on the farm a long time before Johnnie was born.
After Grandpa died, Grandma came to the city to stay
with her grandchildren. But she missed the country,
the orchard and her house. Most of all she missed
her independence. So she decided to return to her farm.

Although Grandma had never been to school and could not read
or write, she ran her farm so well that she always had enough
to live on and extra fruit to give away. She worked very hard
and took care of her house, her flowers, her chickens
and ducks by herself. When the fruit needed harvesting,
she hired workers from the village.

Grandma wore her hair in a bun. She was patient
and never lost her temper. She said she was happy
living alone, but she was even happier on weekends
when her grandchildren came from the city to stay with her.

Grandmother

Where Grandma Lived

When the family arrived each Friday, Grandma stood outside
her house with arms outstretched to hug her grandchildren
as they ran toward her over the little wooden bridge.
Johnnie stopped to pat and pick up Jackie on the way.
Everything in the country seemed green and open
after the crowded city. The smell of flowers
and the country sounds of chickens filled the air.

The older members of the family paraded over the bridge,
carrying bamboo baskets with trays of sugar, coffee,
tea, flour, and cakes Johnnie's mother had made.
Inside, Grandma had tea ready and they all sat down
to *tiffin,* a supper of curry dishes and fruit.

Johnnie was always eager to go to the tiny village
of Bukit Timah just down the road from Grandma's house.
There, all the houses and shops had thatched straw roofs
just like Grandma's. Behind their houses the villagers
grew vegetables, tapioca and yams, and raised chickens, ducks
and pigs. Through the open window of the coffee and noodle shop,
Johnnie saw older people talking and playing *mah-jongg.*

Everyone in the village knew everyone else. While Grandma
shopped at the grocery store or chatted with friends,
Johnnie played with the village children or visited
the iceman. He had a little wagon filled with ice
which he scraped. He used the shavings to make an ice ball
and over it he poured syrup. It was very hard to choose
from the many flavours. The ice ball tasted so good, so cold
and sweet, under the hot tropical sun. Sometimes there was even
a surprise at the centre where the iceman had put a piece
of candied fruit or sweetened beans.

There was often a kite flying overhead for everyone to watch.

Arriving at Grandma's

The Things They Did at Grandma's

At Grandma's house, Johnnie's job was to herd the ducks.
Mornings he took them, waddling and quacking, down
to the pond where they spent the day swimming and diving
for snails, weeds and water hyacinths. He had no trouble
with them in the morning because they loved the pond,
but in the afternoon when he went to bring them home
they didn't want to get out of the water. He had to use
his long bamboo pole to keep them in line.

Sometimes the family walked in Grandma's garden
early in the morning. It was fragrant with flowers:
jasmine, gardenia, frangipani and—sweetest smelling of all—
the *ilang-ilang* which is called the "perfume tree" in Singapore.

Grandma often wore a little jasmine in her hair and Mom
made flower water to wash her face and put in her bath.
Many people say flowers smell best toward evening,
but Mom believed they were best early in the morning.
She gathered the flowers when they were still fresh
with dew and soaked them in cold well water.

At other times the family picked fresh fruit and sat
at a little garden table to eat it. Papaya, bananas
and pineapples grew in Grandma's orchard all year round,
and rambutans, star fruit, pomelo nutmeg, jack fruit,
durians, and breadfruit at special times.

Johnnie rarely had candy, but he loved sugar cane.
Grandma peeled off the tough greenish-yellow outer layers
for him so that he could chew on the pulpy insides.
She pressed out the sweet juice and then added
a few chips of ice to make sugar-cane water.
In the city you could buy it on street corners,
but it tasted best at Grandma's.

Herding the ducks

The Games They Played

In the tropics, clouds burst like balloons.
Rain pours down suddenly and stops just as suddenly.
When Johnnie was caught by a cloudburst,
he grabbed a yam leaf and used it like an umbrella.
It didn't really keep him dry but he enjoyed pretending.
Only the baby chickens seemed to stay dry
under their mother's wing.

All the children liked playing with water.
Grandma had a huge clay tub with dragons painted on it
which she used to collect rainwater to wash clothes.
She let the children race their wind-up boats in the tub,
but told them never to climb in because she was afraid
they'd drown.

When they went fishing in the stream that ran
in front of the orchard, Grandma never worried.
It was shallow and beautiful tropical fish sparkled
in the clear water.

Johnnie and his friends liked to walk barefoot
on the cool sandy bottom and catch the fish
which they put in Grandma's glass pickle jars.
Grandma admired them but said it was cruel
to keep the fish that way. So Johnnie made
everyone put them back into the stream,
to catch again tomorrow maybe.

Racing boats in the big tub

The Work They Did at Grandma's

At harvest time, Johnnie liked to sit under a banana tree
and watch the workers. They hoed the earth, watered it
and picked only the ripe fruit. Pineapples that are left to ripen
on the stalk are delicious and the family enjoyed them at tea.
But Johnnie found bananas much more interesting.

There are over 300 kinds of bananas, some tiny as a thumb,
some big as two feet, all of them good to eat.
After all the bananas are harvested, the tree is cut down
and a new one grows in its place. The leaves are good
for wrapping food; the trunks are chopped up for pig feed.

There was a pig farmer in the village who came to Grandma's
with a handcart to collect banana trunks and yam leaves.
These he chopped up and boiled with bran and grain. He fed
it to the pigs who went crazy over it: they snorted,
slurped, grunted and squealed. Johnnie liked to visit
and watch, and he often brought his own basket of overripe
fruit to feed the pigs. In return the farmer usually brought
Grandma a chunk of pork when he prepared a hog for market.

The mango harvest was difficult and dangerous, and took
several days. The villagers arrived at sunup,
climbed the tall thin trees and very carefully moved out
on the branches. When they had gone as far as they dared,
they picked the fruit. What they couldn't reach they shook
down, and Johnnie had to be careful not to be hit by the falling
fruit. Ripe mangoes are orange, sweet and delicious.
But even the green ones were used by Grandma
to make a pickle called *symbal* that went well with rice.

Midmorning Grandma came out her front door carrying a pot
of rice porridge called *congee* and a kettle of tea. Everyone
climbed down from the trees to rest and enjoy the snack.

Pineapples and bananas

The Things They Ate

Grandma's kitchen was a wonderful place to be,
and Johnnie loved to sit and watch while Mom and Grandma
worked. One whole wall was a built-in cooking area.
The family was Buddhist by religion, and for several days
each month they ate no meat, only vegetables.
Cabbage, mushrooms, cucumbers, bamboo shoots,
winter melons, were cut up, seasoned and cooked,
either mixed together or in separate little bamboo trays
placed one above the other over a steaming *wok*.

Just before the Chinese New Year the kitchen was busiest
of all. For days the women worked making cakes
and cookies. Fish were scaled and cleaned;
ducks and chickens were plucked and cooked.

And there were great delicacies that were very, very difficult
to prepare. Shark's fin was mixed with crab meat to make
one kind of soup; bird's nest soup was made from the lining
of swallows' nests—collected with great skill from the walls
of caves by climbers much admired for their courage.

On the great day, the banquet began about noon and went on
for hours. Johnnie's father sat at the head of the table,
welcoming the guests as they arrived. Each brought
a pair of mandarin oranges as a symbol of health
and prosperity. All the children got gifts of money
wrapped in red paper. Johnnie was glad he was still a child.
When he married he would be a grownup and then
he would have to give little red packages
to the children, instead of receiving them.

The banquet went on for course after course
but the party was not over when the food was finished.
The festivities continued for a whole week.

In Grandmother's kitchen

When Night Came on

Night at Grandma's was full of wonderful scary things.
Sometimes Mom took the children walking
over toward the mountain to see the great swarms of bats
that suddenly came out of their caves to hunt for food.
Some were very big and ate fruit, others were small
and squeaked as they swooped through the air hunting
for insects. Johnnie liked to yell at the bats and pretend
he wasn't afraid but when the bats swooped down
they were all glad Mom was with them.

After supper the children carried stools out on the veranda
to listen to Grandma tell ghost stories.
The stories were very scary and usually told of people
getting lost in cemeteries. The children listened shivering.
Bats flapped their wings among the fruit trees,
and crickets and tree frogs sang.

The children were forbidden to play in cemeteries
and Johnnie wondered if Grandma told the story to make sure
they would obey. As soon as she finished, someone shouted
"Let's go!" and they all ran off to the bamboo grove
to play hide and seek.

Grandma's dog Jackie was left at home because he barked
and gave away the hiding places. But whoever was "it"
was allowed to carry Cat along for company
because the hiders made spooky sounds.

And as it grew darker, the bamboo grove filled with shadows.
Lizards moved on the tree trunks, frogs croaked,
fireflies sparkled and bats swooped in and out.
Finally, it got too dark and too scary, someone shrieked
and everybody ran back as fast as possible to the safety
of Grandma's house.

Bats at dusk

Back in the City

On Sunday night, when Johnnie was taken back to the city, he liked to sit quietly on the sofa in the living room with his own cat. In the family portrait on the wall above him, he was just a baby sitting on his mother's lap; his father and older brother and sister stood beside them.

Everyone was very dignified in the portrait, and Johnnie learned to sit quietly without moving just as if his picture were being taken now. Grandma was not in the portrait, but she was in Johnnie's thoughts.

He liked to remember the things he had done that weekend at Grandmother's house, and then—just before going to bed— to think of the things he would do when he went back next weekend.